CAT
anatomy
and dissection guide

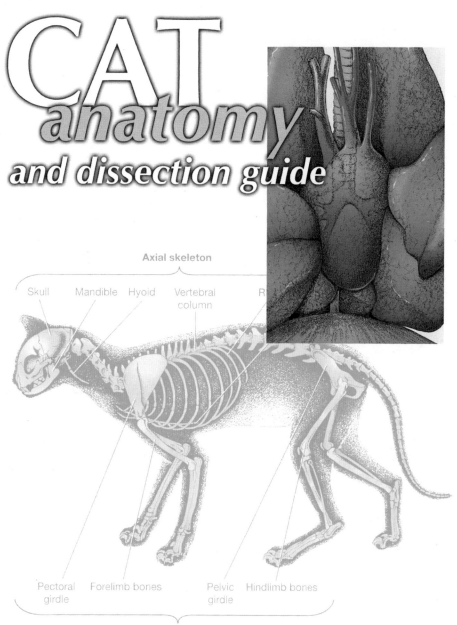

Axial skeleton

Skull Mandible Hyoid Vertebral
column

R

Pectoral   Forelimb bones   Pelvic   Hindlimb bones
girdle   girdle

Appendicular skeleton

Bruce D. Wingerd

bluedoor
flexible & affordable learning solutions

Chief Executive Officer: Jon K. Earl

President, College: Lucas Tomasso
President, Private Sector: Dawn Earl
Regional Manager: Greg Bartell

Senior Production Manager: Connie Dayton
Production Manager: Dan Woods
Digital Solutions Manager: Amber Wahl
Developmental & Production Coordinator: Rhiannon Nelson
Production Assistant: Ben Sweeney
Production Assistant: Erica Rieck
Production Manager: Stephanie Larson
Project Manager: Peggy Li

Consulting Editors: Bruce D. Wingerd, M.S.
                       Suzanne S. Frucht, Ph.D.
                       Anna M. Kats, M.S., Florida Atlantic University
                       Michelle F. Cavallo, M.S., Florida Atlantic University
                       John F. Wiginton, Ph.D., University of Mississippi
                       Stephanie R. Dillon, Ph.D., Florida State University

---

ISBN 978-1-59984-000-0

© 2006 by bluedoor, LLC.

© Cover images by bluedoor, LLC.

Published by bluedoor, LLC
              10949 Bren Road East
              Minneapolis, MN 55343-9613
              800-979-1624
              www.bluedoorpublishing.com

Printed in the United States of America.
10 9

TABLE OF CONTENTS

TABLE OF CONTENTS (cont.)

INTRODUCTION

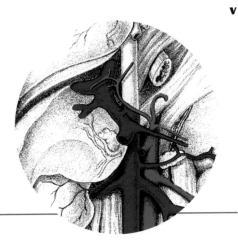

The domestic cat, *Felis catus*, has found a place in the homes and lives of people since approximately 5,000 BC. Without great wonder: the cat is affectionate, intelligent, highly adaptable to a life indoors or outdoors, useful in the removal of rodents that can carry disease, and as this book will demonstrate, useful in providing a learning experience in mammalian anatomy.

Cats are a common site in anatomy labs throughout the world. They are frequently used as a representative quadruped (4-legged) animal, but also as a comparison to the anatomy of humans; for the benefit of this latter audience, this book includes comparisons to human anatomy that are provided in italics. Important terms of cat anatomy are introduced in bold face type, which serves to emphasize them. The purpose of this text is to describe the anatomy of the cat with references to human anatomy, using the learning tool of mammalian dissection.

The use of cats for lessons in anatomic dissection provides students with a close look at mammalian anatomy, and can provide valuable lessons in the technique of dissection. The experience of dissection has merit, for it is a unique "hands-on" approach to the study of anatomy. Going beyond the visual investigation of charts, models, lists of terms, and lectures, dissection engages the student to examine real structures using the additional sense of touch. This practical approach has the potential for opening up new dimensions of learning if it is taught properly, with reverence and respect for life. It is the goal of this text to present cat dissection in a clear, step-by-step manner in an effort to make the learning experience meaningful and effective.

A NOTE ON TERMINOLOGY

The science of anatomy is the study of the structure of an organism and its parts. Its purpose is to answer two basic questions about any structure: What does it look like? and Where is it located? The answers to these questions originate from explanations and descriptions of what is observed. Terminology is an important tool that is used by the anatomist to provide objective, accurate explanations and descriptions. Most anatomical terms are formed from Latin and Greek word parts, providing a universal language of terminology.

The best way to begin your effort of learning the anatomical terminology of the cat is to first learn the terms of direction. These terms are used throughout the book, and provide a universal way of identifying the location of structures. The terms of direction use a standard reference position known as the **anatomical position**. For a quadriped, the anatomical position is defined as standing on all four limbs with the head and tail extended. Throughout this book, descriptions are based on the cat in the anatomical position. The terms of direction include the following:

cranial: toward or pertaining to the head (also called anterior)
caudal: toward or pertaining to the tail or rear (also called posterior)
rostral: the most forward portion of the body

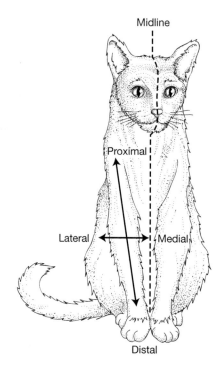

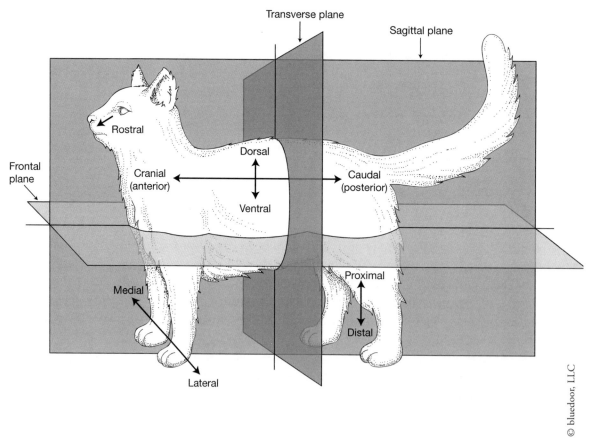

Figure 0.1 – Directional terms and planes.

dorsal: toward the back
ventral: away from the back, or toward the belly
medial: toward the middle or median plane
lateral: away from the middle or median plane
proximal: the point nearest to the central axis
distal: the point furthest from the central axis
superficial: toward the surface
deep: away from the surface
superior: toward the top of a vertical plane
inferior: away from the top of a vertical plane

In addition, several planes of section are often used when describing certain parts. A plane is an imaginary flat surface that extends through the body in a particular direction. A sagittal plane extends vertically to divide the body into right and left portions. A frontal plane also extends in a vertical direction, but it divides the body into front and back portions. A horizontal plane extends at a right angle to the long axis of the body or structure, resulting in cranial and caudal portions. It is also called a transverse plane (or cross section).

c h a p t e r   o n e

THE SKELETAL SYSTEM

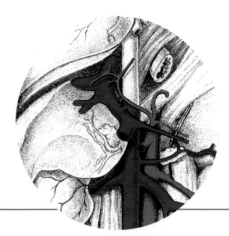

The skeletal system of mammals is composed of the bones and joints. When the bones and joints are combined, they form an articulated structure known as the **skeleton**. Similar to the skeleton of all vertebrates, the skeleton of the cat is an endoskeleton, lying within the soft tissues of the body. It performs several important functions, including support of soft body tissues and maintenance of posture, assistance in movement by serving as rigid attachments for skeletal muscles, protection of vital organs like the brain and heart, storage of calcium and phosphorus in the form of mineral salts, and formation of blood cells within red bone marrow.

DIVISIONS OF THE SKELETON

Similar to all mammals, the skeleton of the cat is divided into two basic divisions: the **axial skeleton**, which contains the bones that lie along the central axis of the body, and the **appendicular skeleton**, which consists of bones lying outside the central axis. Study the complete skeleton of the cat shown in Figure 1.1 to become oriented with its general organization. The list that follows identifies the minor divisions within each skeleton.

Axial Skeleton

Skull: the cranium, facial bones, hyoid bones of the throat, and three small ossicles of the middle ear (35 to 40 total bones form the skull).

Vertebral column: the cervical, thoracic, lumbar, sacral, and caudal vertebrae (52 to 53 vertebrae).

Thorax: the sternum and ribs (8 bones of the sternum and 26 ribs).

Appendicular Skeleton

Pectoral girdle: the shoulder blade and collarbone on each side (4 bones).

Upper limb: the upper arm, forearm, and forepaw on each side (58 total bones).

Pelvic girdle: the os coxae, or innominate, bones (6 bones).

Lower limb: the thigh, shank, and hind paw on each side (52 total bones).

BONES OF THE AXIAL SKELETON

Using the articulated skeleton of a cat and disarticulated bones that may be available in your lab, study the following bones and their major features (Figures 1.2 - 1.21). Note that the bones you are examining are inorganic mineral deposits from living material that has since been eliminated. The bones of the axial skeleton lie along the central axis of the body, and include the skull, vertebral column, and thorax.

The Skull

The skull provides protection for the brain and sensory structures surrounding the brain. It includes the cranium, the facial bones, and the mandible.

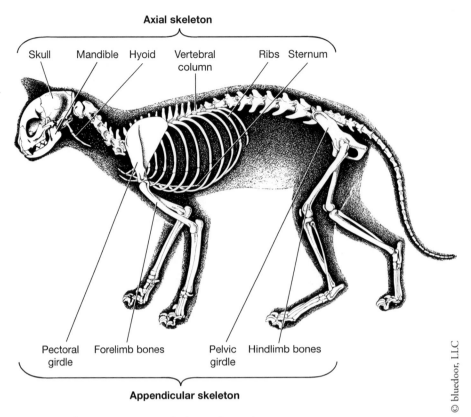

Axial skeleton

Skull   Mandible   Hyoid   Vertebral   Ribs   Sternum
                              column

Pectoral   Forelimb bones   Pelvic   Hindlimb bones
girdle   girdle

Appendicular skeleton

© bluedoor, LLC

Figure 1.1 – Cat skeleton, lateral view.

Bones of the Cranium

The dome-shaped cranium encloses and protects the brain (Figures 1.2 - 1.5). The flat bones that form the cranium are united at immovable fibrous joints, called **sutures.**

Parietal bones: paired bones that form most of the dorsal aspect of the cranium. They are roughly square-shaped, and include a slight ridge that establishes the dorsal limit of the temporal fossa, known as the **temporal line.** In young cats, an **interparietal bone** is also present, located between the parietals at their caudal edge. In adult cats, this bone usually fuses with the parietals.

Frontal bones: paired bones that contribute to the dorsal aspect of the cranium, located rostral to the parietal bones. They extend laterally to contribute part of the orbit, which houses the eye. The **supraorbital** (or **zygomatic) process** is a prominent dorsolateral extension of each frontal bone. Inside the frontal bone is an air-filled cavity, known as the **frontal sinus.**

Temporal bones: the paired temporal bones are the most prominent bones of the cranium's lateral surface. They each consist of three parts: squamous, tympanic, and petrosal.

Squamous: forms the lateral wall of the cranium. It includes an arch-shaped **zygomatic process,** which projects laterally and rostrally; and a groove near the origin of the zygomatic process that provides an articulating surface for the condyloid process of the mandible, called the **mandibular fossa.** Together with the parietal bone, the squamous part of the temporal bone forms the **temporal fossa,** which provides the origin of the temporal muscle.

Tympanic: located ventral from the squamous part of the temporal bone. It includes the rounded **tympanic** (auditory) **bulla,** and a large oval opening leading into the tympanic cavity, called the **external auditory meatus.** In large cats, the malleus (one of three tiny ear ossicles) can sometimes be seen attached to the tympanic membrane (eardrum).

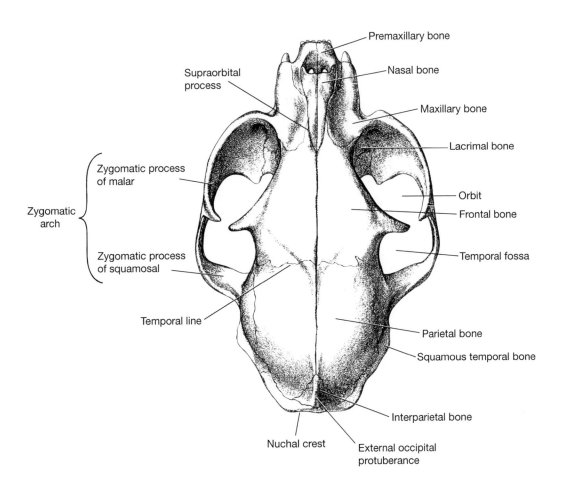

Figure 1.2 – Cat skull, dorsal view.

Petrosal: also known as the petrous portion, it is not visible externally, except for the mastoid process. The **mastoid process** is a prominent, angular, nipple-shaped projection that is located lateral to the tympanic bulla. The interior of the petrosal part of the temporal bone contains the internal ear, or bony labyrinth. *The temporal bone of the human is very similar to that of the cat, with the most obvious difference being a lack of a tympanic bulla in the human and an additional sharp process, known as the styloid process.*

Occipital bone: the single bone that forms the caudal and caudoventral aspect of the cranium. From the caudal view, it resembles an equilateral triangle that has curved borders. The curved borders are the **nuchal crest**, which meet mid-dorsally to form the **external occipital protuberance**. The large opening enclosed by the occipital bone is the **foramen magnum**, which marks the origin of the spinal cord as it emerges from the brain stem of the brain. Lateral to the foramen magnum are the smooth **occipital condyles.** The occipital condyles articulate with the first cervical vertebra, or atlas. Lateral to each condyle is a blunt process called the **jugular process**. Near the base of the jugular process is the **jugular foramen**, which allows passage of the internal jugular vein and three cranial nerves: Glossopharyngeal (CN IX), Vagus (CN X), and Spinal Accessory (CN XI). Medial to the jugular foramen is the **hypoglossal canal**, through which the Hypoglossal Nerve (CN XII) passes.

Sphenoid bone: Anterior to the occipital bone is the single sphenoid bone. Its disarticulated shape is often described as resembling that of a butterfly. The body of the "butterfly" is known as the **basisphenoid**, and the wings are called **alisphenoids**. Two large processes extend anteriorly from the basisphenoid, and

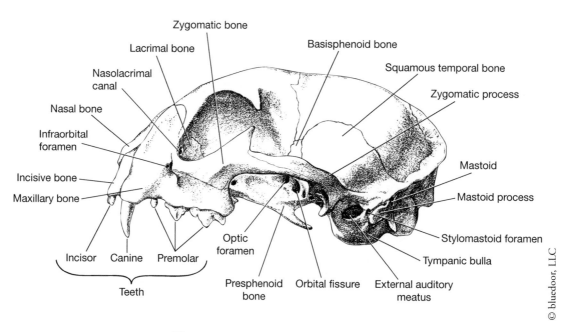

Figure 1.3 – Cat skull, lateral view.

are called **pterygoid processes**. They articulate with the pterygoid bones, and include a narrow lateral projection, known as the **pterygoid crest**. At the base of the pterygoid processes are three openings: the **orbital fissure**, which allows passage of the Oculomotor Nerve (CN III), the Trochlear Nerve (CN IV), the Ophthalmic division of the Trigeminal Nerve (CN V), and the Abducens Nerve (CN VI); the **foramen rotundum**, through which passes the Maxillary branch of the Trigeminal Nerve (CN V); and the **foramen ovale**, through which exits the Mandibular division of the Trigeminal Nerve (CN V). *The human sphenoid bone includes an additional opening, the foramen spinosum, located posterolateral to the foramen ovale.* The dorsal surface of the basisphenoid is shaped like a saddle. The depression of the "saddle" is known as the **sella turcica**, where the pituitary gland is located. Inside the sphenoid is an air-filled space, called the **sphenoidal sinus**.

Presphenoid bone: a single bone that articulates with the anterior border of the basisphenoid of the sphenoid bone. It consists of a body and two wings. The body resembles the shape of an hourglass, and internally contains the

sphenoidal sinuses. The wings extend caudolaterally and resemble small triangles. At the base of each wing is the **optic foramen**, through which passes the Optic Nerve (CN II) and ophthalmic artery. *In the human, the presphenoid is incorporated into the single sphenoid bone, although the features in both the cat and human are in comparable locations.*

Facial Bones

The bones on the rostral part of the skull form the bones of the cat's face (Figures 1.2 - 1.5).

Ethmoid bone: a single, internal bone that forms the bony structures of the nasal cavity. Its major feature is the **ethmoturbinates**, which are scrolled, thin plates of bone that occupy most of the nasal cavity. The thin **perpendicular plate of the ethmoid** separates the two lateral ethmoturbinates. Combined with the vomer, they form the nasal septum that divides the nasal cavity into right and left chambers. *In humans, the superior and middle nasal conchae are homologous with the ethmoturbinates of the cat. The human ethmoid includes a triangular, dorsal projection from the cribriform plate known as the crista galli, which* *provides an attachment for meninges (protective membranes) of the brain. The human ethmoid also includes extensive sinuses, contrary to the ethmoid of the cat.*

Vomer: a single bone ventral to the ethmoid and caudal to the hard palate that forms the upper bony wall of the mouth. The vomer is a thin, narrow bone that contributes to the bony nasal septum.

Premaxillary bones: paired bones at the rostral end of the upper jaw. They form roughly one-sixth of the hard palate (bony roof of the mouth), by way of **palatine processes.** Three incisors arise from each premaxilla. *In humans, two incisors arise from the maxilla; the premaxilla fuses with the maxilla and is not recognized as a separate bone.*

Maxillary bones: paired bones located lateral to the premaxillae. The maxillary bones, or maxillae, form most of the upper jaw and contribute to the hard palate caudally as the **palatine processes of the maxillae.** At the cra-nial border of the maxilla is a bulge known as the **alveolar process,** which accommodates the long root of the canine tooth. An opening called the **infraorbital foramen** penetrates the maxilla about midway, and a **zygomatic process** extends away from the caudal part of the bone.

Palatine bones: paired bones located caudal to the palatine processes of the maxillae. Each palatine bone consists of paired **horizontal plates,** which meet midventrally to form the caudal end of the hard palate. Each horizontal plate is penetrated by an opening called the **sphenopalatine foramen,** which carries the sphenopalatine nerve and blood vessels. Extending caudally are the **pterygoid processes of the palatine,** which articulate with the pterygoid processes of the basisphenoid. *In the human, the pterygoid processes are smaller and closely associated with the greater wings of the sphenoid.*

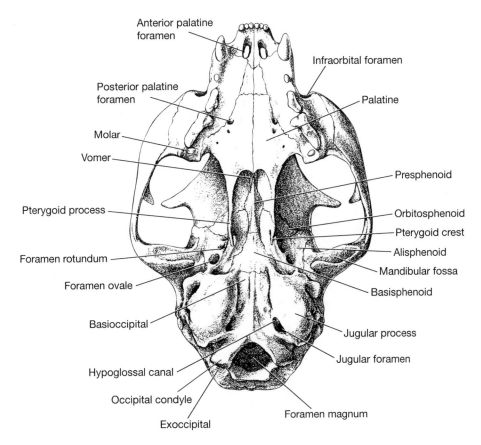

Figure 1.4 – Cat skull, ventral view.

© bluedoor, LLC

Lacrimal bones: paired thin, wafer-like bones that can be found in the rostral portion of the eye orbit. They include a channel called the **nasolacrimal canal**, which is a prominent landmark of the orbit.

Zygomatic bones: paired bones that form the lateral border of the eye orbit. Each articulates with the zygomatic process of the temporal bone caudally and the zygomatic process of the maxillary bone rostrally, forming the zygomatic arch, or cheek prominence.

Nasal bones: paired bones that articulate with the frontal bone at their caudal border, the maxillary bone laterally, and with one another medially.

Incisive bones: small, paired bones in which the incisor teeth are rooted. Each articulates with the maxillary bone along its caudolateral border, with the nasal bone caudolaterally, and with the opposite incisive bone medially. *The human incisive bones fuse with the maxillary bones soon after birth.*

Surface Features of the Skull

Now that you've become familiar with the individual bones of the skull and their major features, examine a complete skull. Although the surface is relatively smooth, there are sutures, ridges, and openings that break up the topography.

A suture is an immovable articulation that binds two bones with tough, fibrous connective tissue. Classified as synarthrotic joints, they occur between opposing skull bones and are named with the bones with which they are associated.

Frontal suture: between the frontal bones.

Sagittal suture: between the parietal bones.

Coronal suture: between the frontal and parietal bones.

Squamosal suture: between the parietal bone and squamous part of the temporal bone.

Lambdoidal suture: between the parietal bones and the interparietal bones and occipital bones.

Intermaxillary suture: between the premaxillary and maxillary bones.

Nasomaxillary suture: between the nasal and maxillary bones.

Sphenofrontal suture: between the sphenoid and frontal bones.

The ridges of the skull include the prominent **nuchal crest** of the occipital bone, which was described previously, and the faint **temporal line.** The temporal line is the origin of the broad tem-

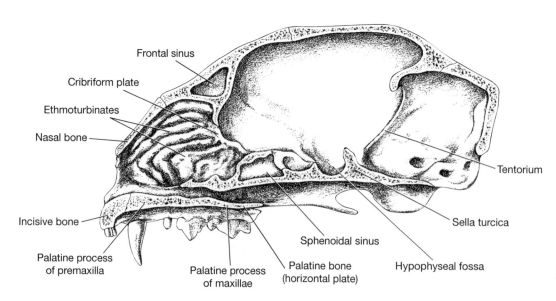

Figure 1.5 – Sagittal section of cat skull, lateral view.

© bluedoor, LLC

poralis muscle, extending from the caudal margin of the postorbital process and curving over the frontal bone onto the parietal bone, meeting with the temporal line of the opposite side in a V-shaped pattern to terminate at the nuchal crest.

Openings of the skull include the large **external nares** (nostrils) that open into the nasal cavity, the **internal auditory meatus** in the petrosal part of the temporal bone, and the **foramen magnum** of the occipital bone. Numerous smaller openings have been described, most of which permit passage of cranial nerves and blood vessels.

Note the eye **orbit** on the lateral side of the skull. This prominent concavity is formed by the frontal, maxillary, lacrimal, zygomatic, and palatine bones rostrally, and by the sphenoid and presphenoid bones caudally. The openings on the caudal side of the orbit include the **optic canal** (in the sphenoid bone), the **orbital fissure** (from the basisphenoid and presphenoid bones), the **foramen ovale** (in the sphenoid bone), and the **foramen rotundum** (in the sphenoid bone). On the rostral side of the orbit are the **sphenopalatine foramen** (in the palatine bone) and the **nasolacrimal canal** (in the lacrimal bone).

Mandible

The lower jaw or **mandible** completes the bones of the head (Figure 1.6). The bones forming the mandible are paired, and are called **dentary** or **mandibular bones,** which articulate at the **intermandibular symphysis.** *In the human, the two dentary bones fuse within two years after birth to produce a single bone, the mandible.* The mandible contains the ventral dentition and articulates with the skull at the **mandibular fossa.** At the caudal end are a pair of processes, the **condyloid processes,** each of which articulates with the mandibular fossa of the temporal bone. Notice that the condyloid processes in the cat are shaped like a bar, which is typical among carnivores due to their need to hold struggling prey and also to reduce rotary and lateral grinding movements. *In contrast, the condyloid processes in the human are ovoid, which is expected for an omnivore who rarely needs to restrain prey and needs to rotate and grind food more often.*

Observe the mandible in a lateral view, and notice that the cranial end includes a smooth, rounded bar. Known as the **body,** it contains two or three **mental foramina,** which allow passage of the mandibular division of the Trigeminal Nerve (CN V). The caudal end of the mandible expands to form the **ramus.** The dorsal part of the ramus contains the **coronoid process,** which is the site of the temporalis muscle insertion. The triangle-shaped depression below it is the **coronoid** (masseteric) **fossa,** which serves as the insertion for the masseter muscle of the jaw.

The mandible's medial side is relatively smooth, except at the symphysis, where the opposite dentery articulates. The **mandibular foramen** provides passage of the mandibular division of the Trigeminal Nerve (CN V).

The teeth are anchored in sockets along the dorsal **alveolar border.** In each dentery bone are three small **incisors** and a single **canine** rostrally, and two **premolars** and one **molar** caudally. The space between the canine and first premolar is called the **diastema.**

The Vertebral Column

The vertebral column consists of a series of articulating bones, known as the **vertebrae,** which are divided into five regions: cervical, thoracic, lumbar, sacral, and caudal. The vertebrae are joined by shock-absorbing pads called **intervertebral discs.** Together, they provide support along the axial plane of the body and serve as attachments to the pectoral girdle and pelvic girdle.

Common Features of Vertebrae

The vertebrae of the five regions can be distinguished from one another by characteristics that are common to each region. However, all vertebrae share some features. Each vertebra is composed of a solid **body** or **centrum,** which forms the main ventral support for the spinal cord. A large opening dorsal to the body, the **vertebral canal,** carries the spinal card and its membranes. Dorsal to the vertebral canal is a pair of **laminae,** whose dorsal extensions form the **spinous process.** Lateral to the vertebral canal are the paired **pedicles,** and extending from the body in a lateral direction on both sides are the **transverse**

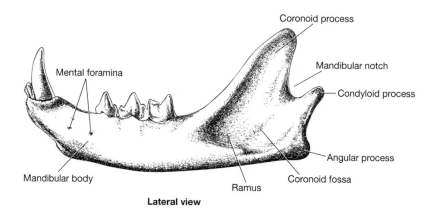

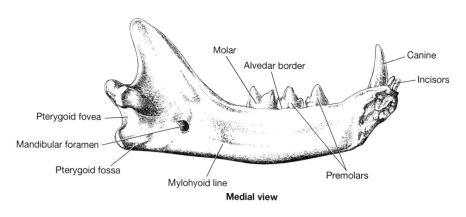

Figure 1.6 – Mandible, lateral view and medial view.

processes or **diapophyses**. At the cranial end of each vertebra are two pairs of processes that articulate with adjacent vertebrae: the **prezygapophyses**, whose articulating surfaces face dorsally, and the caudal **postzygahypophyses**, whose articulating surfaces face ventrally.

Cervical Vertebrae

The first and second cervical vertebrae, the atlas and axis, have features that distinguish them from all other vertebrae. The ring-like **atlas** (Figure 1.7a) lacks a body and spinous process. Instead, it includes broad, wing-like transverse processes, and **atlantal foramina** located dorsal to the prezygapophysis. The first spinal nerve and the vertebral artery pass through these small openings. The **transverse foramen** passes through the transverse process of the atlas, and carries the vertebral artery and vein. *The human atlas is very similar to that of the cat, except it does not include atlantal foramina.*

The **axis** (Figure 1.7b) resembles a blacksmith's anvil, when viewed laterally. It is characterized by a large spinous process that overhangs the **arch of the atlas** and a prominent process that extends cranially called the **odontoid process**, or **dens**. The odontoid process provides a "finger" that enables the "ring" of the atlas to pivot around for rotation of the head on the neck. *The human axis includes a bifurcated spinous process that is grooved on the posterior side.*

The remaining five cervical vertebrae are similar to one another and include typical vertebral features, with some exceptions (Figure 1.7c). The spinous process of the third cervical vertebra is very small, while those of the fourth through seventh increase in size as the thoracic region is approached. Also, the seventh lacks vertebral foramina. *In the human, cervical vertebrae two through six contain short, bifurcated spinous processes, while that of the seventh is long and single. All seven cervical vertebrae include transverse foramina.*

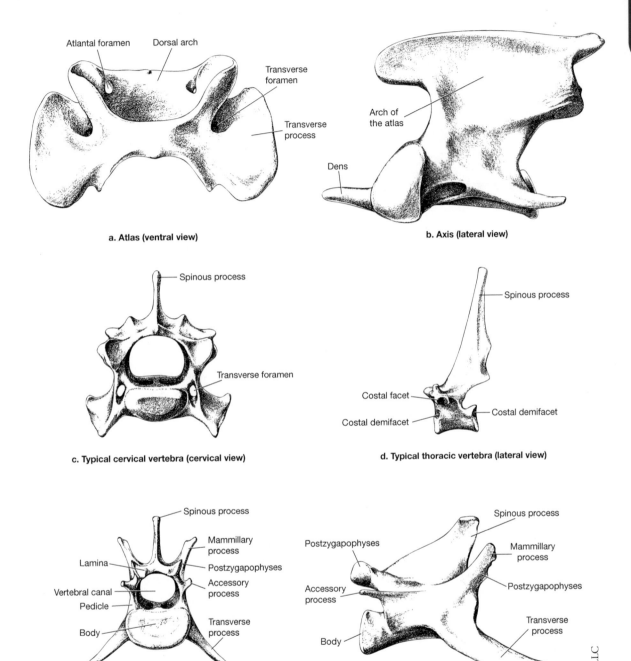

a. Atlas (ventral view)

Atlantal foramen
Dorsal arch
Transverse foramen
Transverse process

b. Axis (lateral view)

Arch of the atlas
Dens

c. Typical cervical vertebra (cervical view)

Spinous process
Transverse foramen

d. Typical thoracic vertebra (lateral view)

Spinous process
Costal facet
Costal demifacet
Costal demifacet

e. Typical lumbar vertebra (caudal view)

Spinous process
Mammillary process
Lamina
Postzygapophyses
Accessory process
Vertebral canal
Pedicle
Body
Transverse process

f. Typical lumbar vertebra (lateral view)

Postzygapophyses
Spinous process
Mammillary process
Accessory process
Postzygapophyses
Body
Transverse process

© bluedoor, LLC

Figure 1.7 – Representative vertebrae.

Thoracic Vertebrae

Thoracic vertebrae are specialized to articulate with the ribs of the thoracic cage. Cats usually have thirteen thoracic vertebrae, each of which shares common features and includes the features of a typical vertebra, with certain notable exceptions (Figure 1.7d). An **articular facet** is located on the ventral surface of the transverse process, which articulates with the tuberculum of a rib. Also, **demifacets** on the body articulate with the capitulum of a rib. The elongation of the spinous processes make them distinct, and point caudally in the first nine or ten thoracic vertebrae. At the eleventh or twelfth thoracic vertebra, the angle abruptly changes to point cranially; this vertebra is often called the **anticlinal vertebra**. The spines of the remaining thoracic vertebra follow this orientation. *In humans, there are 12 thoracic vertebra, and all spinous processes point in the same direction.*

Lumbar Vertebrae

The seven **lumbar vertebrae** are the largest vertebrae, increasing in size toward the caudal end (Figure 1.7e, f). They include the features common to all vertebrae, with the following notable exceptions. Extending in a cranial direction from both sides is a **pleurohypophysis**, which is embryonically derived from the transverse process and rib. Also, **accessory processes** are narrow extensions of bone located ventral to the postzygopophyses that can be found in the first five lumbar vertebrae, and blunt **mammillary processes** are present on all seven vertebrae. *In the human, there are five lumbar vertebrae. They are similar to those of the cat, except the bodies are relatively more substantial in size and there are no pleurohypophyses present.*

Sacrum

The **sacrum** provides a supportive center for the pelvic girdle and is a complex of three fused vertebrae in the adult (Figure 1.8a), but separate bones in the kitten. The three fused vertebrae decrease in size caudally, without losing the features of the preceding bone. Notice that the pleuropophyses are fused into a single lateral structure, and **dorsal** and **ventral foramina** are present between each fused vertebra. The foramina permit passage of spinal nerves. A large opening extends through the length of the sacrum as a fusion of the adjacent vertebral canals, and is called the **sacral canal** or **sacral hiatus**. *The human sacrum is composed of five fused vertebrae, and does not include pleuropophyses.*

Caudal Vertebrae

The **caudal vertebrae** form the skeleton of the tail, and are the smallest and most variable in number of the vertebrae (Figure 1.8b). The more cranial bones include the typical features of vertebrae, whereas the more caudal vertebrae lose them to become cylindrical bones dominated by the centrum. Notice the presence of **hemal processes** on the ventral side of the bodies. *Human caudal vertebrae are much less numerous, numbering three to five and are called coccygeal vertebrae that are usually fused in the adult to form the coccyx.*

The Hyoid

The hyoid is a complex of bones that are derived from ancestral gill supports. In mammals, the hyoid apparatus is located ventral to the larynx and at the base of the tongue. It serves as the site of origin for muscles of the tongue and larynx.

The hyoid is H-shaped and consists of a **body** that forms the bar of the H, two **lesser horns**, or **cornua**, forming the upper arms of the H, and two **greater horns**, or **cornua**, that form the two lower arms of the H (Figure 1.9). In the adult cat, each lesser horn consists of four small bones, while each greater horn is a single fused bone. *In the human, the hyoid apparatus is a single fused bone, although it is also H-shaped, and similarly contains a body and a pair of greater cornua and a pair of lesser cornua.*

The Sternum

The **sternum** forms the ventral aspect of the thoracic cage, extending along the ventral midline of the thorax. It is a slim and elongate structure that is composed of a linear series of **sternebrae** (Figure 1.10), which are individual, articulating bones. It is divided into three regions: a cranial **manubrium** that resembles an arrowhead, a middle **body** consisting of six similar, articulated sternebrae, and a caudal **xiphisternum** consisting of a single elongated sternebrae. At the caudal end of the **xiphisternum** is a cartilaginous piece called the **xiphoid process**. Along intervals of the sternum are **costal cartilages,** which extend to the ribs. The first pair of costal cartilages connect the manubrium to the first pair of ribs, and the following eight pairs connect the sternal body to ribs. *By contrast, the human sternum is flat in shape and consists of a superior manubrium, a middle body representing the fusion of four sternebrae, and an inferior xiphoid process that is usually ossified in adults.*

The Ribs

There are thirteen pairs of **ribs** in the cat. The first nine pairs are **vertebrosternal ribs,** since they articulate with the sternum by way of costal cartilages. The caudal four pairs of ribs vary with the individual cat, but usually include the first three pairs attached by cartilage to each other or to the costal cartilage of the ninth pair. These ribs are called **vertebrochondral ribs.** The final pair has no sternal connection, and are therefore called vertebral, or "floating", **ribs.**

The shape and features of each rib are very similar, although their overall length differs (Figure 1.11). Each rib is a curved, flattened rod with a proximal end that includes a **head,** or **capitulum,** which articulates with the demifacets on the bodies of two adjacent thoracic vertebrae. A second process on each rib is the **tubercle,** which articulates with the transverse process of a vertebra. The tubercle decreases in size caudally, and is absent from the last two or three pairs of ribs. Between the head and the tubercle is a slightly narrowed area called the **neck.** The proximal curved part or **angle** of the rib blends into the distal part known as the **shaft.** A small, pointed projection, called the **angular process,** is located on the angle of the rib. Along the angle of each rib on the caudal side is a shallow depression known as the **costal groove.** *In contrast to the cat, the human ribcage contains twelve pairs of ribs, including seven vertebrosternal ribs, three vertebrochondral ribs, and two vertebral ribs.*

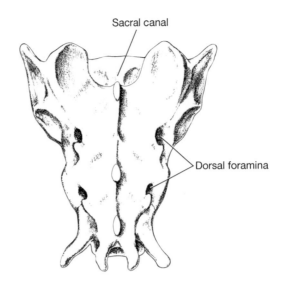

a. Sacrum (dorsal view)

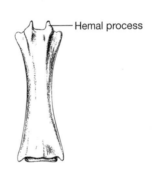

b. Caudal vertebra (dorsal view)

© bluedoor, LLC

Figure 1.8 – Sacrum and caudal vertebrae.

BONES OF THE APPENDICULAR SKELETON

The bones of the appendicular skeleton form the bones of the pectoral girdle and forelimbs, and the pelvic girdle and hindlimbs.

Pectoral Girdle

Only two bones form the pectoral girdle to provide attachment and support for the forelimbs: the clavicle and the scapula.

Clavicle

The **clavicle** in quadrupeds that rely on running to survive is a drastically reduced bone, often

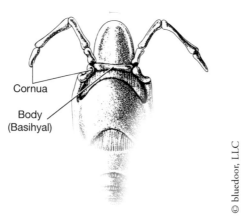

Figure 1.9 – Hyoid bone.

embedded within the shoulder muscles. In the cat, it is a slender, curved bone with a slight enlargement on the sternal end (Figure 1.12). It articulates medially with the manubrium of the sternum and laterally with the acromion process of the scapula. *In humans, the clavicle is a much more robust bone, with a slight sigmoid curvature and pronounced articulating surfaces.*

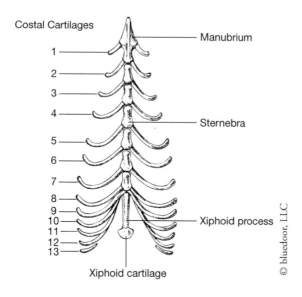

Figure 1.10 – Sternum and costal cartilages.

Scapula

The **scapula** is a flat, blade-like triangular bone (Figure 1.12). At its ventral side, it articulates with the head of the humerus by way of a concave surface known as the **glenoid fossa**. Extending medially from the glenoid fossa is a beak-like projection called the **coracoid process**, and laterally is the **supraglenoid tubercle**. A prominent lateral

ridge, known as the **scapular spine**, extends from the glenoid fossa to a pointed projection called the **acromion process**. Just dorsal from the acromion process is a blunt process, the **metacromion**. The scapular spine divides the lateral surface of the scapula into an anterior

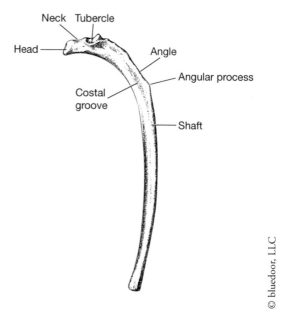

Figure 1.11 – Rib.

supraspinous fossa and a posterior **infraspinous fossa**. The medial surface of the scapula is mostly flat, and is called the **subscapular fossa**. Its borders include a curved **dorsal** or **vertebral border**, a **cranial border**, and a **caudal** or **axillary border**. *With the exception of the relative increase in size of the infraspinous fossa in the human scapula, the cat and human features are very similar.*

Bones of the Forelimbs

The bones of the forelimbs include the humerus, ulna, radius, carpals, metacarpals, and phalanges.

Humerus

The **humerus** is the proximal long bone of the anterior appendage, providing support for the muscles of the brachium and shoulder (Figure 1.13). It articulates with the scapula at the glenoid fossa at its proximal end, and with the radius and ulna at its distal end. The proximal end consists of a smooth, rounded **head**. Medial to the head is a roughened area called the **lesser tuberosity**, and lateral to the head is the larger **greater** tuberosity. The **bicipital groove** (intertubercular sulcus) separates the two areas, and carries the tendon of the biceps brachii muscle.

The distal end of the humerus is dominated by a large, medial process called the **trochlea**, and a lateral, rounded process known as the **capitulum**. Medial to the trochlea is a **medial epicondyle**, and lateral to the capitulum is a **lateral epicondyle**. A slight depression is located proximal to the trochlea, and is called the **coronoid fossa**. A similar depression proximal to the capitulum is the **radial fossa**. Proximal to the medial epicondyle is an oval opening known as the **supracondylar foramen**, which carries the median nerve and brachial blood vessels. On the dorsal side of the humerus proximal to the trochlea is a prominent depression, the **olecranon fossa**, which articulates with the olecranon of the ulna to form the elbow joint.

Extending from the lateral epicondyle to the approximate midpoint of the shaft of the humerus is a narrow ridge, called the **supracondylar ridge**. Extending from the proximal end of the humerus to converge at roughly the same area of the shaft is the **pectoral ridge** and the **deltoid ridge** (or **deltoid tuberosity**). All three ridges serve as attachment sites for muscles.

The humerus of the human is very similar to that of the cat, with the exception of an absence of the supracondyloid foramen and the presence of an anatomical neck (distal to the head of the humerus).

Radius

The **radius** is one of two bones supporting the forearm, or antebrachium (Figure 1.14). It extends from the lateral proximal end of the humerus to the medial distal part of the carpus, thereby crossing over the ulna. The proximal end of the radius consists of a **head**, which is slightly concave for articulation with the capitulum of the humerus. The head is circumscribed with a narrow, smooth articular circumference, which articulates with the notch of the ulna. Distal to the head is the **neck**, and distal to the neck is the **radial tuberosity** that receives the tendon of the biceps brachii. A roughened surface, called the **interosseous crest**, extends distally from the tuberosity.

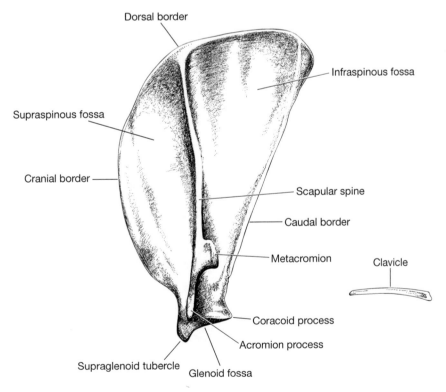

Dorsal border

Infraspinous fossa

Supraspinous fossa

Cranial border

Scapular spine

Caudal border

Metacromion

Clavicle

Coracoid process

Acromion process

Supraglenoid tubercle

Glenoid fossa

© bluedoor, LLC

Figure 1.12 – Scapula (lateral view) and clavicle.

The distal end of the humerus contains a pointed projection on the medial side, called the **styloid process.** Proximal to the styloid process is a depression that articulates with a carpal bone known as the scapholunate, and on the lateral surface is a small concave margin that articulates with the ulna. *The radius of the human shares the same major features as that of the cat.*

Ulna

The **ulna** extends parallel to the radius in the antebrachium. The proximal end is known as the **olecranon,** and articulates with the olecranon fossa of the humerus (Figure 1.15). The olecranon also is the insertion site of the triceps brachii tendon. Distal to the olecranon on the ventral side is a broad excavation, called the **semilunar (trochlear) notch.** The notch receives the trochlea of the humerus. Distal to the semilunar notch is an anterior projection, the **coronoid process,** which forms the medial margin of a concave surface called the **radial notch.** The radial notch articulates with the head of the radius.

The distal end of the ulna consists of a sharp lateral process known as the **styloid process.** This peg-like process articulates with the cuneiform

and pisiform of the carpals. Along the lateral side of the ulnar shaft is a ridge known as the **interosseous crest,** which attaches to a tough sheet of connective tissue that attaches to the radius. *The ulna of the human shares the same major features as that of the cat.*

Carpals and Manus

The **carpals** include seven small bones that form the wrist, or **carpus** (Figure 1.16). They are arranged into two rows, a proximal set of three and a distal set of four. The medial and largest of the proximal row is the fused scaphoid and lunate, called the **scapholunate.** *In the human, the scaphoid and lunate are separate bones.* The middle bone of this row is the **cuneiform,** *which is also called the triquetral in the human.* The most lateral bone of the proximal row is called the **pisiform.** The distal row contains, from medial to lateral, the **trapezium, trapezoid, capitate,** and **hamate.** The distal bones articulate with the metacarpals of the hand on their distal surface.

The bones that form the hand, or **manus,** consist of five **metacarpals** and the **phalanges** that form the five digits. There are two phalanges in the thumb (digit #1) and three in each of the other four digits. In the cat, retractile claws extend from each distal phalanx, *which are not found in humans and other non-feline mammals.*

Pelvic Girdle

The pelvic girdle is formed by the os coxae. It receives additional support by the sacrum, which is attached to the os coxae at the sacroliliac joints.

Os Coxae

The **os coxae** are also known as the **innominate bones.** They are paired bones, right and left, that are joined to form the pelvic girdle. Each innominate bone is a complex of three individual bones: the **ilium,** the **ischium,** and the **pubis** (Figure 1.17 a, b). In a juvenile cat, the three bones are separated by sutures, but the sutures become less apparent in adult cats as the bones become fused. The pelvic girdle is formed by the innominate bones articulating along the medial surfaces of the

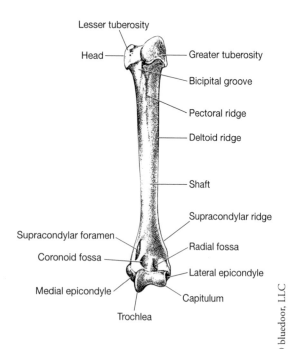

Lesser tuberosity

Head

Greater tuberosity

Bicipital groove

Pectoral ridge

Deltoid ridge

Shaft

Supracondylar ridge

Supracondylar foramen

Radial fossa

Coronoid fossa

Lateral epicondyle

Medial epicondyle

Capitulum

Trochlea

© bluedoor, LLC

Figure 1.13 – Humerus (ventral view).

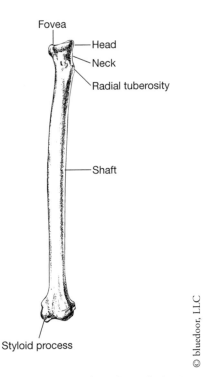

Figure 1.14 – Radius (dorsolateral view).

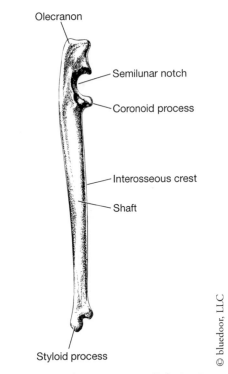

Figure 1.15 – Ulna (ventromedial view).

© bluedoor, LLC

pubis and ischium, forming the **pubic symphysis** and **ischial symphysis.**

The ilium forms the cranial portion of each innominate bone. It is a wing-shaped bone with a concave lateral surface known as the **wing of the ilium.** The dorsal part of the wing is thickened, and is called the **iliac crest.** The ventral part becomes thickened also to form the **body,** which contributes to the round concavity known as the **acetabulum.** The cranial part of the ventral aspect is known as the **ileopectineal line,** which continues onto the pubic surface to the pubic symphysis.

The ischium forms the dorsal portion of the innominate bone. It consists of a thickened, broad **body** and a thinner **ramus.** The roughened surface of the body at its posterior end is the **tuberosity of the ischium,** and near the cranial end is the prominent **spine of the ischium.**

The pubis is the ventral part of the innominate bone. The portion of the pubis that is continuous with the ramus of the ischium is known as the **ramus of the pubis,** which terminates as the **pubic tubercle.** The thicker **body** forms an approximate right angle with the ramus, and joins the body of the ilium.

The large opening of each innominate bone is called the **obturator foramen,** and is formed by the ischium and pubis. The obturator nerve passes through the foramen, although most of the opening is closed by fibrous connective tissue. As described previously, the large bowl-shaped

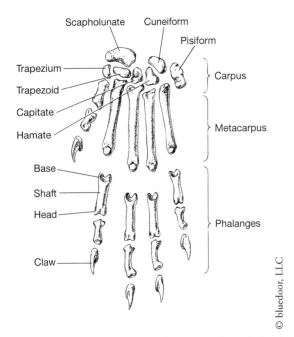

© bluedoor, LLC

Figure 1.16 – Carpals and manus (dorsal view).

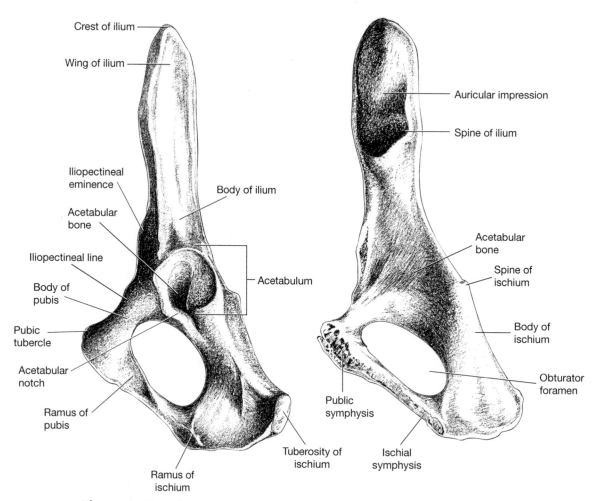

Crest of ilium

Wing of ilium

Iliopectineal eminence

Acetabular bone

Body of ilium

Iliopectineal line

Body of pubis

Acetabulum

Pubic tubercle

Acetabular notch

Ramus of pubis

Ramus of ischium

Tuberosity of ischium

Auricular impression

Spine of ilium

Acetabular bone

Spine of ischium

Body of ischium

Obturator foramen

Public symphysis

Ischial symphysis

Figure 1.17a – Os coxa, or innominate bone (left lateral, right medial views).

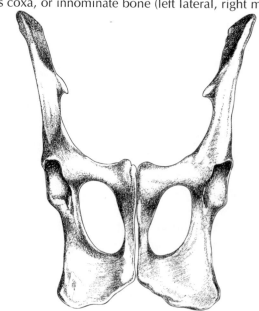

Figure 1.17b – Paired os coxae (ventral view).

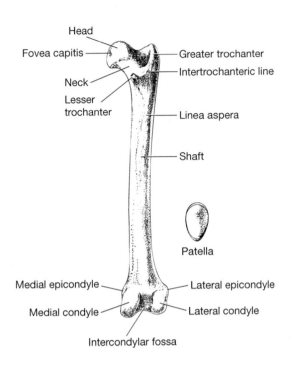

Figure 1.18 – Femur (ventral view).

© bluedoor, LLC

depression is the acetabulum, which receives the head of the femur. The acetabulum is formed by contributions from each of the three parts of the innominate bone.

The innominate bones of the human differ from the cat due to the posture differences of bipedal gait. The innominate bones are in a more upright position in the human, and the ilium has a greater width relative to overall size. Also, the innominate bones are sexually dimorphic in humans; that is, the female ilium flares laterally, while the male ilium is more upright, and the angle between the opposing pubic bones is more obtuse in the female to form the birth canal.

Bones of the Hindlimb
The hindlimb bones include the femur of the thigh, tibia and fibula of the lower hindlimb, tarsals of the ankle, and metatarsals and phalanges of the pes.

Femur
The **femur** is the long, proximal bone of the hindlimb that supports the thigh region (Figure 1.18). The proximal end of the femur contains a prominent ball-shaped projection known as the **head.** An irregular depression on the medial side of the head is called the **fovea capitis.** The head articulates with the acetabulum of the innominate, and the fovea capitis is the attachment site of a ligament that helps hold the head of the femur in place. Distal to the head is a constricted **neck.** Lateral to the head and neck is another prominent projection known as the **greater trochanter,** which is the attachment for major muscles of the hip. A depression medial to the greater trochanter is called the **trochanteric fossa.** Extending from the greater trochanter is a ridge called the **intertrochanteric line,** which terminates at a lateral process called the **lesser trochanter.**

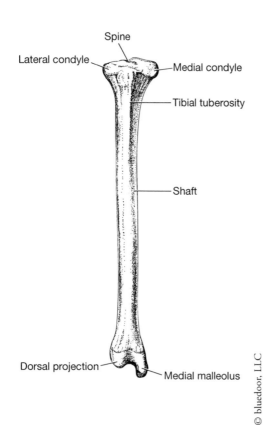

Spine
Lateral condyle
Medial condyle
Tibial tuberosity
Shaft
Dorsal projection
Medial malleolus

© bluedoor, LLC

Figure 1.19 – Tibia (ventral view).

A long ridge extends from the greater trochanter down the dorsolateral aspect of the femur shaft, known as the **linea aspera**, which is an attachment site for muscles of the thigh.

The distal end of the femur also contains important features. The two prominent, rounded projections that dominate the distal end are the **medial condyle** and **lateral condyle**. They articulate with the proximal end of the tibia. A deep notch on the dorsal side separates the condyles, and is called the **intercondylar fossa**. The **lateral** and **medial epicondyles** are processes located on each corresponding condyle, and provide sites of muscle attachment. Note that the surface area between the condyles on the dorsal side is smooth. This is the **patellar surface**, which is joined with the **patella**, or kneecap. The patella is known as a sesamoid bone, since it lies within tissues other than bone. It is surrounded by the large tendon of the quadriceps femoris muscle. *The femur of the human is very similar, sharing each of the major features described.*

Tibia

The **tibia** is the longer, more robust bone of the lower hind leg or crus (Figure 1.19). As such, it bears most of the weight of the hind limb. The proximal end of the tibia is triangular, with a **medial** and **lateral condyle** forming the base of the triangle. They contain smooth surfaces that articulate with the condyles of the femur. A two-pointed projection known as the **spine** separates the articular surfaces. Between the tibial condyles on the dorsal side is a **popliteal notch**, and on either side of the condyles are a **medial** and **lateral tuberosity**. On the ventral side, a process called the **tibial tuberosity** is located between the medial and lateral condyles.

The distal end of the tibia includes two prominent projections. The longer of the two is the **medial malleolus**, and the shorter is the **dorsal projection**. On the dorsolateral surface is a smooth surface, which articulates with the fibula. The lower surface of the distal end is concave, allowing articulation with the ankle. *The tibia of the human is very similar, sharing each of the major features described for the cat.*

Fibula

The slender, more fragile bone of the lower hindlimb is the **fibula** (Figure 1.20). The proxi-

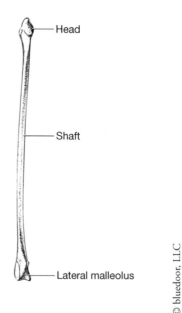

Head
Shaft
Lateral malleolus

© bluedoor, LLC

Figure 1.20 – Fibula (ventral view).

mal end of the fibula includes an irregularly shaped **head**, with a medial surface that is smooth for articulation with the lateral surface of the tibia. The distal end includes a prominent sharpened projection called the **lateral malleolus**, which contains smooth articular surfaces on its medial side for articulation with the tibia and talus. *The human fibula shares the same features as that of the cat.*

Tarsals and Pes

Similar to the carpals, there are seven **tarsals** in the cat (Figure 1.21). However, the tarsal bones vary in size. The medially located **talus** is the largest, due to its requirement to bear much of the weight of the ankle. The talus articulates with both the tibia and the fibula. Lateral to the talus is the **calcaneus,** which is the longest bone of the ankle and forms the heel. Distal to the talus is the **navicular.** The distal four tarsal bones lie in a row. From medial to lateral, they are the **medial cuneiform**, the **intermediate cuneiform**, the **lateral cuneiform**, and the **cuboid.**

The hind foot or **pes** consists of five **metatarsals**, which articulate with the distal row of tarsals. The first metatarsal is greatly reduced in the cat, while the remaining four are elongated bones that each articulate with a digit. Each digit consists of three **phalanges.** Similar to the manus, the distal phalanx includes a retractable claw.

The human has two major differences in the bones forming the ankle and foot. There is a prominent first digit, or "big toe", in the human not seen in the cat. Secondly, the entire foot of the human is in contact with the ground from heel to toe, and is, therefore, horizontal, while the cat contacts the ground only with the toes while walking or running, resulting in a more vertically inclined morphology.

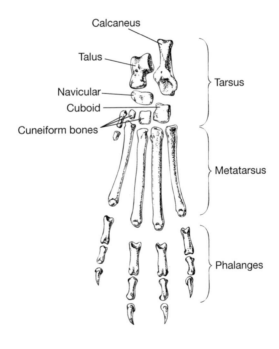

© bluedoor, LLC

Figure 1.21 – Tarsals and pes (dorsal view).

CHAPTER REVIEW

A. Answer the following multiple-choice questions by circling the most correct answer.

1. Which of the following are components of the axial skeleton?
   a. bones of the skull
   c. interparietals and mandible
   b. sternebrae
   d. all of the above

2. The large, flat bones forming the cat skull include the
   a. parietal bones
   c. ethmoid bone
   b. maxilla
   d. clavicle

3. The external auditory meatus passes through the
   a. tympanic portion of the temporal bone
   c. squamous portion of the temporal bone
   b. sphenoid bone
   d. frontal bone

4. The optic foramen penetrates at the base of the wing of the
   a. ethmoid bone
   c. presphenoid bone
   b. frontal bone
   d. sphenoid bone

5. The first cervical vertebra is ring-like, and is called the
   a. axis
   c. zygopophyses
   b. atlas
   d. thoracic vertebra

6. The ribs are connected to the sternum by way of
   a. intervertebral discs
   c. the neck of each rib
   b. costal cartilages
   d. thoracic vertebrae

7. A single bone that is formed by the fusion of three vertebrae and provides support for the pelvic girdle describes the
   a. os coxae
   c. ilium
   b. caudal vertebrae
   d. sacrum

8. The acromion process can be found on the
   a. humerus
   c. scapula
   b. ulna
   d. femur

9. The head of the femur articulates with the
   a. obturator foramen
   c. acetabulum
   b. sacrum
   d. tibia at the knee joint

10. The smaller bone of the lower hindlimb is called the
    a. fibula
    c. calcaneus
    b. tibia
    d. lateral cuneiform

B. Complete the sentences below by providing the missing terms from the chapter material.

1. The _____ _____ is a pointed process of the petrous portion of the temporal bone.

2. The foramen magnum penetrates the _____ bone and transmits the spinal cord.

3. The orbital fissure and sella tursica are prominent features of the _____ bone.

4. The vomer and the perpendicular plates of the _____ bone form the nasal septum.

5. The _____ bones form most of the upper jaw and contribute to the hard palate.

6. The _____ _____ is a fibrous joint between the frontal and parietal bones.

7. The _____ vertebrae are specialized to articulate with the ribs.

8. The trochlea and capitulum are large projections on the distal end of the _____.

9. The os coxae are formed by the mergeance of the _____, _____, and pubis.

10. The largest tarsal bone of the cat is called the _____.

C. Answer the following descriptive and critical-thinking questions with a brief explanation in the spaces provided.

1. Describe the skeletal features of the manus and pes of the cat that enable them to "walk on tiptoes".

   _____

   _____

   _____

   _____

   _____

2. Explain the major differences between the cranium of the cat and the cranium of the human.

   _____

   _____

   _____

   _____

c h a p t e r   t w o

PRINCIPLES AND TECHNIQUES OF DISSECTION

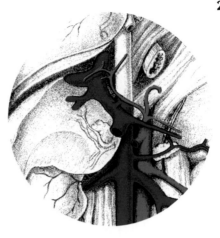

Dissection of preserved specimens has proved to be an effective method of studying anatomical structures. It allows unique "hands-on" experience in exploring organs and organ systems that cannot be realistically obtained in any other way. This chapter is intended to give you a foundation of dissection skills from which to begin, and includes a discussion of dissection techniques and instruments, a survey of the external features of the cat, and a step-by-step guide to the skinning procedure.

PRINCIPLES OF DISSECTION

The primary goal of dissection is to bring into view structures than cannot otherwise be seen in their normal environment. The goal is achieved by working from the exterior surface of the specimen inward. Once the body structures are exposed, they may be examined and identified. Ideally, the complete dissection of your specimen will enable you to study all the internal structures in their proper location within the body.

The level of success that you achieve in the dissection process will depend on the following factors:

- *The time you put into the project.* One aim of dissection is to display each structure fully, clearly, and cleanly. This is a time-consuming process, but it is time well spent. You cannot achieve this goal by rushing through the procedure. But remember that the time you are allowed to spend in the lab is limited. Therefore, make efficient use of it. Read the text and plan your dissection strategy before class, and avoid spending large amounts of time tracing smaller structures before you have identified the larger picture.
- *The level of care and patience that you exercise.* Dissection is not merely "cutting up" an animal; it is a careful process of separating different parts from each other. Great care must be exercised at all times to avoid damaging structures before they have been identified. To keep unnecessary damage to a minimum, thoroughly examine the area you are about to cut into or pull apart before doing so. Do not cut or remove any structure before you have identified it. Also, follow the dissection guide step by step, and do not cut until you have been instructed to do so.
- *Your choice and use of dissection instruments.* Correct tools are a necessity whenever precision is desired. For example, you would choose to use a knife rather than a chainsaw to cut into your birthday cake. Dissection is no different! The following list describes the common dissection instruments, including their proper uses:

Blunt probe: a rigid 5-inch steel instrument with a blunt, usually bent tip. This is very useful for tearing through connective tissue, teasing muscles apart, and separating fragile structures from their attachments.

Scissors: usually 4 to 6 inches long, with the end of one blade pointed and the other rounded. Scissors should be used to cut through skin, cut muscles through their center (called bisect), and make other large, clean cuts through major structures.

Scalpel: usually 5 inches long, with replaceable blades. The scalpel should be used to gently scrape away connective tissue and fat, cut through tough fibrous tissues, and make small incisions. But be careful: Not only can the blade cut your finger very quickly, it can also cause irreparable damage to the specimen, so use it sparingly.

Needle probe: a 3-inch needle usually attached to a wooden handle. The needle probe can be used as a pointer, or to attach the specimen to the dissecting tray.

Forceps: about 5 inches long, with handles transversely ridged to prevent fingers from slipping. The ends should be blunt and rounded, and the gripping surfaces grooved. Forceps are used to grasp small objects and to remove (pull away) connective tissue.

Protective gear: because the preservative can be irritating to your skin and damage your clothes, you should wear protective latex gloves and a lab coat or apron while dissecting.

EXTERNAL FEATURES OF THE CAT

It's time now to begin preparing for dissection, the first step of which is to remove the skin. But first, let's examine the external features of your specimen. Preserved cats are usually shipped to schools within individual plastic bags that contain the cat and some residual preservative fluid. The fluid is present to maintain a moist environment, so the preserved tissues remain soft and damp. Carefully remove the specimen from the bag, while retaining the fluid. When you return the cat to the bag after a day's work at dissection, the fluid will be available to keep the cat as moist as possible.

Lay the cat onto a dissecting tray on its dorsal side (ventral side up). Notice the following external cat features (Figure 2.1):

Body regions: the main regions of the cat are typical of a mammal, and include the head, neck, trunk, limbs, and tail.

Head & neck: the head provides a concentration of paired sensory structures, including the **pinnae** (external ears), the **eyes**, the **superior palpebrae** (upper eyelids) and **inferior palpebrae** (lower eyelids), and the **nostrils** (external nares). Also notice the **vibrissae**, or whiskers, that arise from the cheek area, and the **nictitating membrane** that originates in the lower medial corner of the eye. The **neck** supports the head and connects the head to the trunk.

Trunk: the trunk includes a cranial **thoracic region**, a middle **abdominal region**, and a caudal **pelvic region**. The ventral side of the thoracic region, or thorax, is the **pectoral region**, and the dorsal side is simply called the **back**. Along the ventral surface of the trunk in the thoracic and abdominal regions are two rows of paired **nipples**, which are associated with mammary glands. At the posterior end of the pelvic region is the genital region in both sexes. Evaluate the **genital region** to determine the sex of your specimen. A male can be determined if you can feel the testes enclosed within the scrotum. The penis is very small and completely enclosed within a sac, so you will not be able to find it without dissection. If you are unable to feel the testes, your cat is a female; if so, find the **urogenital aperture**. At the base of the tail is the opening to the digestive tract, known as the **anus**.

Limbs: as a typical quadruped mammal, the cat has four limbs–two upper forelimbs and two lower hindlimbs. Note the smooth pads that provide cushioning during walking and running, and the retractable claws at the end of each digit. The depression below the shoulder (the armpit) is the axilla.

Tail: the tail of the cat is covered with variable amounts of fur, and is useful as a rudder and balance beam during locomotion. You may have noticed that cats may also use their tail for communication, since it is tactile (sensitive to touch).

SKINNING THE CAT

The cat will be skinned completely during this procedure. Ideally, you will remove the skin in a single piece that can be retained and used to cover the specimen when it is not undergoing dissection. Before removing the skin, observe several areas on the body where skin may have been removed to facilitate the injection of blood vessels (the blood vessels were injected with a liquid plastic latex dye before the specimen was shipped to your campus to highlight the vessels). It is quite common for the neck to be exposed, since it is the usual site of latex injection.

Follow the dissection instructions carefully using the step-by-step directions, which are illustrated in Figure 2.2:

1. With the cat on its dorsal surface, pull the skin at the base of the neck to separate it from underlying tissues, and carefully make a shallow incision with your scalpel, just deep enough to break through the skin. Begin your cut at the base of the neck about one-half inch left or right of the midventral line (to avoid cutting any muscles whose origin or insertion is on the midline).

2. Continue your incision from cranial to caudal. As you do so, insert either an index finger or a probe beneath the skin and break the connective tissue that attaches the skin to the underlying muscle layer. To avoid cutting the muscle

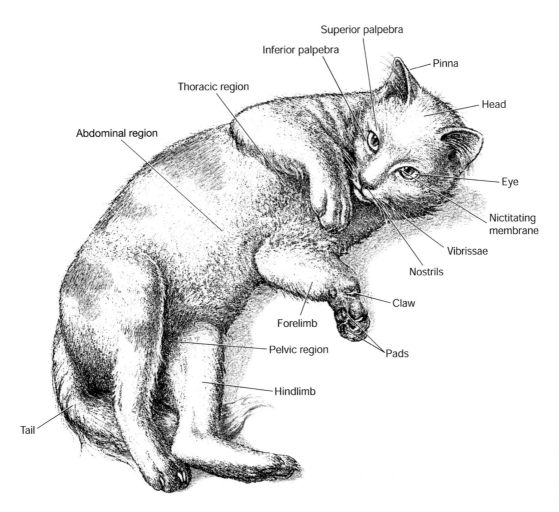

© bluedoor, LLC

Figure 2.1 – External features of the cat.

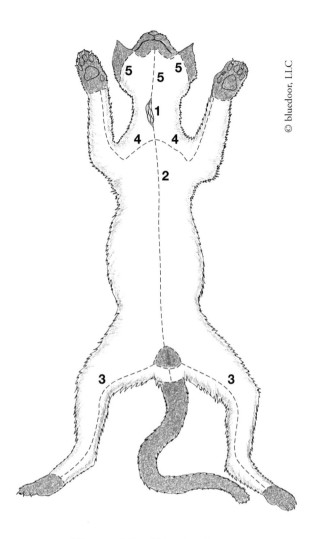

Figure 2.2 – Skinning the cat.

layer, pull the skin upward slightly as you cut. If your specimen is a female that was pregnant recently, you may encounter the swollen mammary glands that will appear as light brown, pancake-like masses between the skin and muscle layers. Remove these glands with the skin. Continue cutting caudally until you reach about 2 inches from the cranial end of the hindlimb.

3. From the caudal end of your midventral incision, continue cutting caudally, but angle the cut down the midline of one of the hindlimbs. Continue this cut down the hindlimb to a point just proximal to the digits. Once there, cut a circle around

the pes. Then, repeat this for the opposite hindlimb. As you cut, remember to carefully separate the skin from the muscle layer with a finger or probe, and lift the skin slightly upward to avoid cutting into the muscles. If your specimen is a male, use caution as you cut near the genital region, since the spermatic cord is embedded within the fat and connective tissue of the groin area beneath the skin.

4. Return to the thoracic region and make an incision from the midventral cut that you made previously, starting from the middle of the thorax and cutting to the right upper limb along its medial aspect. Once you reach the manus, cut a circle around it just proximal to the origin of the digits. Be very cautious to avoid cutting into a thin muscle that adheres close to the skin on the radial side, the brachioradialis muscle. Make a similar cut down the opposite forelimb.

5. Return to your first incision in the neck, and continue the cut cranially to the chin. Then cut along the line of each jaw. Extend the cut around the base of the cranium.

6. Now you're ready to remove the skin. Carefully pull the skin away from the specimen, starting at the hindlimbs and forelimbs. Be very careful as you skin the forelimb to avoid pulling away a superficial blood vessel, the cephalic vein, which passes from the lateral shoulder to the manus. Once the limbs have been skinned, pull the skin from the thoracic region, beginning at the neck. As you skin the trunk, notice an extensive dermal muscle known as the cutaneous maximus. It is especially visible in the axillary (armpit), pectoral, and abdominal regions. This muscle causes the skin to twitch when it is irritated, and is lacking in the human. Remove the cutaneous maximus with the skin. As you do so in

the axillary region, you will need to cut its attachment to underlying muscles.

7. With the skin removed from the trunk and appendages in a single piece, return to the head and neck regions. Remove the skin of the neck first, pulling it cranially toward the heard. Note another dermal muscle, the platysma, which adheres closely to the neck and head muscles. The platysma is well developed in humans. It is preferable to remove this muscle with the skin. The skin of the head region is thicker than that of other areas of the body; to remove it, you may need to scrape your scalpel below the skin as you pull the skin away from the body. Continue the midventral incision to the base of the mandible, and outline the mouth, nose, eyes, and ears, then continue to the midline of the forehead. Loosen the skin from its underlying attachments, then pull it away to remove it.

8. With the skin fully removed from your specimen, you must now clean up the body before continuing into the dissection. Carefully remove fat tissue that adheres to the muscle surfaces by picking away with your forceps. There is usually a large fat deposit in the groin area; if you are working on a male, use caution when removing the fat here to avoid damaging the thin, white spermatic cord that passes through the groin. Do not cut into the muscle or fascia (fascia is a white sheet-like connective tissue covering the muscles). Also, remove any remaining remnants of the cutaneous maximus and platysma.

You are now ready to begin dissecting the muscular system, which is presented in the next chapter (Chapter 3). Remember to keep your cat specimen wrapped in its skin (or a damp towel) and sealed in a plastic bag when not in use. This will help prevent it from drying out and, thus, prolong its use.

CHAPTER REVIEW

A. Answer the following multiple choice questions by circling the most correct answer.

1. The primary goal of dissection is to
   - a. practice cutting through tissues
   - b. complete the task quickly
   - c. bring internal structures into view
   - d. become familiar with the instruments

2. The level of success you achieve in dissection is determined by
   - a. how much patience and care you exercise
   - b. the proper use of instruments
   - c. how much time you invest
   - d. all of the above

3. A rigid instrument with a blunt tip is called a:
   - a. scalpel
   - b. scissors
   - c. blunt probe
   - d. forceps

4. An instrument that is used for grasping and pulling is called:
   - a. scalpel
   - b. scissors
   - c. blunt probe
   - d. forceps

5. To bisect a muscle, you should use:
   - a. a sharp scalpel
   - b. ridged forceps
   - c. a needle probe
   - d. scissors

6. The pinnae, vibrissae, and nictitating membrane may all be found on the:
   - a. neck
   - b. trunk
   - c. head
   - d. hindlimb

7. The trunk contains which three body parts?
   - a. head, neck, and thorax
   - b. thoracic, abdominal, and pelvic regions
   - c. back, belly, and thighs
   - d. all of the above

8. What is the preferred instrument to use when skinning a cat?
   - a. scalpel
   - b. scissors
   - c. needle probe
   - d. forceps

9. The limbs are attached to the:
   - a. pelvic region
   - b. pectoral region
   - c. trunk
   - d. tail

10. When cutting through the skin, it is important to:
    - a. avoid cutting too deep
    - b. cut quickly
    - c. use a sharp scalpel
    - d. avoid cutting the fur

B. Complete the sentences below by providing the missing terms from the chapter material.

1. A _____ _____ is a useful instrument for separating muscles and other structures.

2. When pinning a structure down to a wax tray, you should use _____ _____.

3. The superior and inferior palpebrae are also known as the _____.

4. The ventral side of the thorax is known as the _____ region.

5. The posterior end of the pelvic region is called the _____ region.

6. The depression opposite the shoulder is the _____.

7. The brown, pancake-like masses in the pectoral region of a pregnant female are the _____.

8. The extensive dermal muscle adhering to the skin is called the _____ _____.

9. A smaller dermal muscle in the neck area is called the _____.

10. If the cuts have been made properly, the skin should be removable in a _____ _____.

C. Answer the following descriptive and critical thinking questions with a brief explanation in the spaces provided.

1. Why should the skin be retained after removal from the cat's body? _____

   _____

   _____

   _____

   _____

   _____

2. Why do you suppose over-use of a scalpel can lead to a poor dissection? _____

   _____

   _____

   _____

   _____

3. What benefit does performing a dissection provide to the learning process? _____

_____

_____

_____

_____

_____

_____

c h a p t e r   t h r e e

THE MUSCULAR SYSTEM

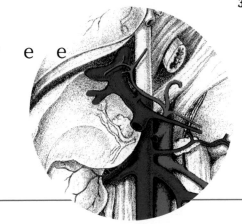

The muscular system consists of skeletal muscle tissue and its associated connective tissue, blood vessels, and nerves. Skeletal muscle cells, or **muscle fibers**, are arranged in multiple parallel bundles to form the muscle unit. Typically, a muscle unit consists of a central fleshy region known as the **belly** and extensions of connective tissue. The muscle is connected to bone. Contraction of muscle produces body movement when the bone to which it is attached is shifted in position.

The connective tissue of a muscle is an extensive network of dense, fibrous connective tissue known as **fascia**. A muscle is attached to a bone by its fascia, rather than by actual muscle fibers. The narrow band of fascia that extends from a muscle to the bone is called a **tendon**. Some muscles are attached to bone by a broad, thin sheet of fascia known as an **aponeurosis**. Typically, a muscle is attached to two bones by tendons or aponeuroses.

The primary function of the muscular system is to provide skeletal movement. Movement is produced when a muscle contracts. During the contraction of a muscle, one end of the muscle moves the bone to which it is attached as the muscle shortens in length. The opposite end of the muscle remains stationary. The attachment of the tendon or aponeurosis to the bone that is mobile during a contraction is called the **insertion**. Conversely, the attachment of the tendon or aponeurosis that is held stationary is the **origin**. In the case of limb muscles, the origin is usually proximal and the insertion is distal. In some muscles that are capable of several actions, the origin and insertion may be reversible.

Muscles are capable of producing a variety of movements, which are called **actions**. The primary actions include:

- Flexion: decrease in the angle at the joint between articulating bones
- Extension: decrease in the angle at the joint
- Adbuction: movement away from the body's midline
- Adduction: movement toward the body's midline
- Rotation: movement around a central axis
- Supination: lateral rotation of the manus upward
- Pronation: medial rotation of the manus downward
- Eversion: rotation of the sole of the pes outward
- Inversion: rotation of the sole of the pes inward
- Circumduction: rotation of a limb around a central axis

Most actions are the result of a combination of muscles working in a coordinated group, rather than the result of individual muscle contraction. The muscles that produce an action directly are known as **prime movers**, which are assisted by additional muscles known as **synergists**. Muscles that assist the primary action by stabilizing the joint or the stationary bone are called **fixators**. In some actions, a muscle must relax in order for the prime mover to be effective; these muscles are known as **antagonists**.

In this chapter you will study the muscular system of the cat through dissection. Each major muscle is listed according to its regional location.

MUSCLE DISSECTION

Muscle dissection involves the careful separation of muscles from each other. This is possible because the fibers of each individual muscle are held together by a sheath of fascia and ordinarily run in the same general direction between attachments. The visibility of individual muscles is enhanced by the different directions that fibers run in adjacent muscles. Since you have cleaned the fat and extraneous tissue from your cat after having skinned it, you should be able to observe the direction of fibers of many of the superficial muscles.

Using a blunt metal probe to break the surrounding connective tissue, you will be able to separate individual muscles in order to observe them more clearly. To separate individual muscles, look at the muscles carefully and note the fiber directions. Remember that a single muscle usually contains fibers that run parallel, setting it apart from other muscles. Once you've distinguished a muscle, insert the probe between it and adjacent muscles and work the instrument inward until the probe tip resurfaces at the opposite cleavage line of each muscle. If the cleavage lines are not clearly visible, gently pull the muscles apart with your fingers until they appear.

You should follow each muscle to its points of origin and insertion as far as is practical. This is done by inserting the probe through both cleavage lines bordering a muscle and sliding the probe laterally along the muscle's length, while pulling the muscle slightly outward (away from the cat's body). The probe will break through the connective tissue between adjacent muscles without causing any damage if this step is done correctly.

Once you have separated and identified all of the superficial muscles of a region, you must **transect** them in order to examine the underlying deep muscles. Transection, or bisection, is performed by making a cut transversely near the center of the muscle belly (perpendicular to the muscle length), leaving sufficient muscle attachment at the points of origin and insertion for later identification. The transected superficial muscles may then be **reflected** by pulling the ends backward toward their points of attachment, which reveals the deep muscles. You should dissect for deep muscles on one side of your cat specimen only. This will leave the superficial muscles on the opposite side intact for later study.

SUPERFICIAL MUSCLES OF THE TRUNK

We will begin our study of muscle anatomy by dissecting the superficial muscles of the trunk, starting on the ventral side and followed by the dorsal side. The muscles of the trunk include the pectoral muscles, abdominal muscles, and back muscles.

Superficial Pectoral Muscles

With your cat specimen on its dorsal side, identify the muscles of the pectoral region. In general, these muscles draw the forelimb toward the midline (adduction).

PECTOANTEBRACHIALIS: the most superficial muscle of the chest, it is a thin, narrow muscle extending from the midline of the body to the proximal end of the humerus (Figure 3.1). Its action is adduction of the forelimb. *This thin muscle is not found in humans.*

PECTORALIS MAJOR: includes a superficial portion and a deep portion (Figure 3.1). The superficial portion is a thin, flat muscle similar in width to the pectoantebrachialis and partially deep to it. It extends from the midventral line and manubrium to the shaft of the humerus. The deep portion is located beneath the superficial portion, and is thicker and wider. To see it completely, transect and reflect the pectoralis major on one side. It originates from the cranial half of the sternum and inserts at the proximal third of the humerus. The primary action of both portions is adduction of the forelimb.

PECTORALIS MINOR: a thick, fan-shaped muscle that extends beneath and caudally to the deep portion of the pectoralis major

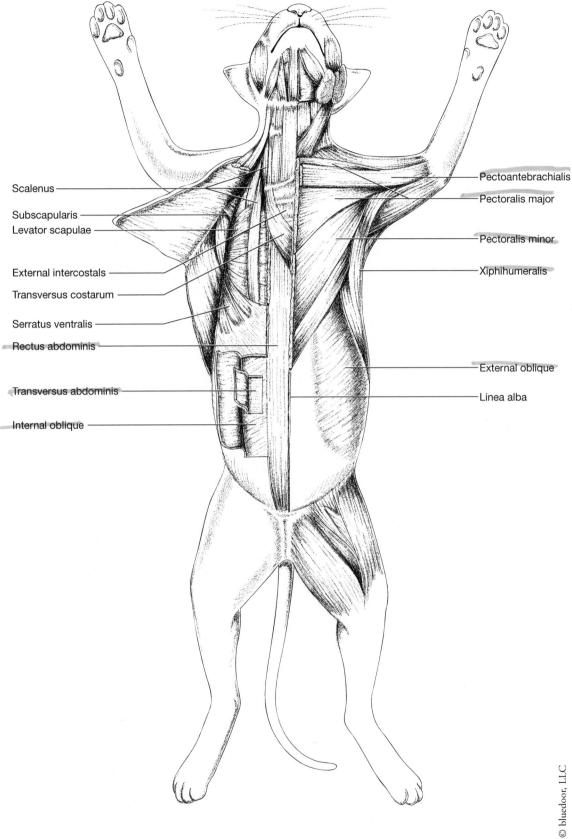

Scalenus

Subscapularis

Levator scapulae

External intercostals

Transversus costarum

Serratus ventralis

Rectus abdominis

Transversus abdominis

Internal oblique

Pectoantebrachialis

Pectoralis major

Pectoralis minor

Xiphihumeralis

External oblique

Linea alba

© bluedoor, LLC

Figure 3.1 – Ventral muscles of the cat.

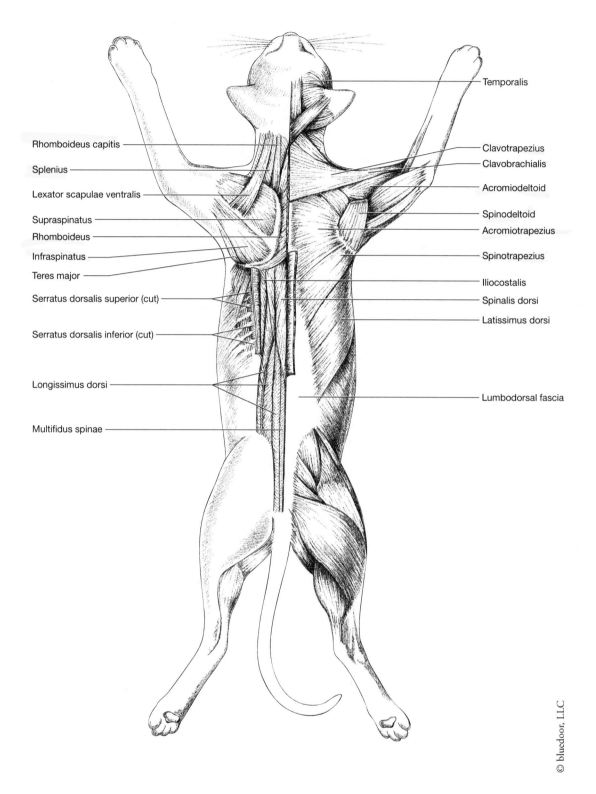

Forelimb

Temporalis

Rhomboideus capitis

Splenius

Lexator scapulae ventralis

Supraspinatus

Rhomboideus

Infraspinatus

Teres major

Serratus dorsalis superior (cut)

Serratus dorsalis inferior (cut)

Longissimus dorsi

Multifidus spinae

Clavotrapezius

Clavobrachialis

Acromiodeltoid

Spinodeltoid

Acromiotrapezius

Spinotrapezius

Iliocostalis

Spinalis dorsi

Latissimus dorsi

Lumbodorsal fascia

Figure 3.2 – Dorsal muscles of the cat.

(Figure 3.1). On one side, carefully cut through the deep portion of the pectoralis major to observe the pectoralis minor. It originates from the six sternebrae, or sometimes the xiphoid process, and inserts at the ventral border of the humerus. The action of the pectoralis minor is adduction of the forelimb.

XIPHIHUMERALIS: located along the caudal border of the pectoralis minor, it is a long, thin muscle extending from the xiphoid process to the ventral border of the humerus. Because it parallels the pectoralis minor, some believe it is actually a part of it. It functions as a synergist with the pectoralis muscles in adduction of the forelimb. *The xiphihumeralis muscle is absent in humans.*

Superficial Abdominal Muscles

The muscles of the abdomen compress the abdominal region. They include three sheet-like muscles that are thin and cover an extensive area, and a single band-like muscle that extends along the ventral midline. The three thin muscles form three layers that can be viewed by cutting a three-sided opening, like a window, through one side in the flank region. Make your window roughly 1-inch long on each side, and reflect the superficial layers to reveal all three muscles. Note that the abdominal muscles are separated into right and left portions by a longitudinal line of white connective tissue, known as the **linea alba** (*white line* in Latin).

EXTERNAL OBLIQUE: the most superficial of the three sheet-like muscles supporting the abdominal wall, its fibers extend craniodorsally (Figure 3.1). It originates from the lumbodorsal fascia of the caudal ribs and inserts at the sternum and along the linea alba. The action of the external oblique is compression of the abdomen.

INTERNAL OBLIQUE: located immediately deep to the external oblique, its fibers extend in a caudodorsal direction (Figure 3.1). Its origin and insertion is in common with the external oblique. The internal oblique compresses the abdomen.

TRANSVERSE ABDOMINIS: the deepest of the three extensive abdominal muscles, its fibers

extend nearly transversely from the origin and insertion (Figure 3.1). It originates from the aponeurosis of the caudal costal cartilages, lumbar vertebrae, and ventral border of the ilium and inserts in common with the two oblique muscles along the linea alba. It compresses the abdomen.

RECTUS ABDOMINIS: a long band of muscle that extends parallel to the linea alba on either side (Figure 3.1). It is enclosed within a sheath of fascia, formed by the aponeuroses of the three abdominal sheet muscles. Its origin is the iliac crest and it inserts at the cartilage of the fifth through seventh ribs and the xiphoid. The rectus abdominis compresses the abdomen and flexes the trunk. *In humans, the rectus abdominis is reduced at its anterior end, and is commonly known as the "six-pack" muscle of the abdomen due to the ridges that form from the aponeuroses, which cross it at intervals.*

Superficial Back Muscles

Turn your cat over onto its ventral side to expose the muscles of the back. The superficial back muscles contribute to actions involving the shoulders and upper arms.

CLAVOTRAPEZIUS: a flat, wide muscle that covers much of the lateral aspect of the neck (Figure 3.2). It originates from the middorsal fascia of the seventh cervical vertebrae and inserts at the clavicle. The primary action of the clavotrapezius is forward extension of the humerus. *In humans, it is represented by the superior portion of the large trapezius.*

CLAVOBRACHIALIS: a muscle that is a continuation of the clavotrapezius into the forelimb (Figure 3.2). Also referred to as the clavodeltoid, it originates from the clavicle and inserts at the lateral surface of the ulna near the semilunar notch in common with the brachialis. It flexes the forearm, or antebrachium. *There is no equivalent muscle in humans.*

ACROMIOTRAPEZIUS: a very thin trapezoid-shaped muscle of the cranial back (Figure 3.2). A thin, whitish fascia that attaches to the middorsal line from the spine of the axis bone to the fourth thoracic vertebra serves as the origin.

The insertion is the metacromion and spine of the scapula. It adducts the scapula. *The acromiotrapezius of the cat is represented by the central portion of the trapezius in the human.*

SPINOTRAPEZIUS: a triangle-shaped muscle that forms the caudal third of the trapezius group in the cat (Figure 3.2). Separate this muscle along its caudodorsal border from the latissimus dorsi (the large, flat muscle of the lower back). The spinotrapezius originates from the spinous processes of the thoracic vertebrae and inserts at the fascia of the supraspinatus and infraspinatus muscles. It pulls the scapula caudally. *It is represented by the inferior portion of the trapezius in the human.*

LATISSIMUS DORSI: the large, flat muscle of the back that is located immediately caudal to (and slightly covered by) the spinotrapezius (Figure 3.2). The latissimus dorsi originates from the fourth or fifth thoracic vertebrae to the sixth lumbar vertebra, and inserts at the medial surface of the humerus. The latissimus dorsi pulls the forelimb dorsocaudally.

MUSCLES OF THE NECK AND HEAD

Muscles of the Neck

The muscles of the neck mainly assist in moving the head and its structures, such as the lower jaw and tongue. Some muscles of the neck act upon the throat region to move the larynx or hyoid bone. Turn your cat over on its dorsal side and begin studying the muscles of the neck on the ventral aspect.

STERNOMASTOID: a prominent V-shaped muscle on the ventral side of the neck (Figure 3.3). Its origin is the cranial border of the manubrium, and it inserts on the lambdoidal ridge and mastoid process of the temporal bone. When the sternomastoids from each side contract simultaneously, they flex the head. Individual contraction rotates the head. *Its equivalent in the human is the sternocleidomastoid, which originates from the clavicle in addi-*

tion to the sternum. Thus, the sternocleidomastoid is a combination of the sternomastoid and the cleidomastoid (described next) in the cat.

CLEIDOMASTOID: a flat muscle that is located dorsolateral to the sternomastoid (Figure 3.3). It originates from the mastoid process of the temporal bone and inserts at the clavicle. The cleidomastoid rotates the head when the clavicle is held stationary, and moves the clavicle cranially when the head is held stationary.

STERNOHYOID: a slender muscle extending along the midventral line of the neck (Figure 3.3). It originates from the first costal cartilage and inserts at the hyoid bone. The sternohyoid retracts the hyoid bone.

DIGASTRIC: a thick muscle extending along the ventral border of the mandible (Figure 3.3). Its origin is the mastoid and jugular processes of the temporal bone, and it inserts at the medial ventral border of the mandible. Its action is depression of the mandible. *The human digastric includes two components: an anterior belly and a posterior belly. The anterior belly parallels the digastric of the cat, while the posterior belly originates from the mandible.*

MYLOHYOID: a small, thin muscle with fibers that extend transversely across the two dentery bones of the mandible (Figure 3.3). The right and left mylohyoids are separated by a thin line of fascia (called the **median raphe**). With a scalpel, cut through the median raphe and reflect one of the mylohyoids toward the mandible. The origin is from the medial surface of the mandible, and the insertion is the median raphe. It elevates the floor of the mouth.

STYLOHYOID: a very small, slender band that extends over the dorsal surface of the digastric muscle from medial to lateral. The stylohyoid is covered with connective tissue, which must be scraped away with great care in order to observe it (Figure 3.3). Its origin and insertion is at the hyoid bone, and its action is elevation of the hyoid bone.

STERNOTHYROID: transects and reflects both bands of the sternomastoid and sternohyoid muscles. The sternothyroid is a deep, slender muscle located slightly dorsal to the sternohy-

THE MUSCULAR SYSTEM

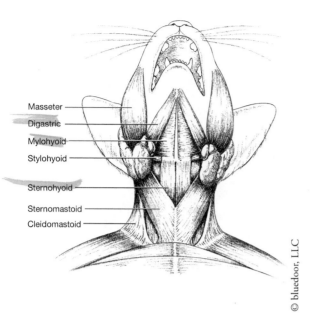

Masseter
Digastric
Mylohyoid
Stylohyoid
Sternohyoid
Sternomastoid
Cleidomastoid

© bluedoor, LLC

Figure 3.3 – Superficial muscles of the neck (ventral view).

oid and lateral to the trachea (Figure 3.4). Its origin is the first costal cartilage and it inserts at the thyroid cartilage of the larynx. It retracts the hyoid bone. *The human sternothyroid originates from the manubrium of the sternum, rather than the first costal cartilage, although the action is similar to that of the cat: retraction of the larynx.*

THYROHYOID: a deep, small, narrow muscle extending along the lateral aspect of the larynx (Figure 3.4). Its origin is the thyroid cartilage of the larynx on the lateral side, and it inserts at the hyoid bone. It protracts the larynx.

CRICOTHYROID: a small, flat muscle on the central surface of the larynx that lies deep to the sternohyoid (Figure 3.4). The cricothyroid originates from the cricoid cartilage of the larynx and inserts at the nearby thyroid cartilage. It regulates the tension exerted on the vocal cords during sound production.

GENIOHYOID: a deep, narrow muscle located along the median raphe immediately deep to the mylohyoid (Figure 3.4). Its origin is the ventral surface of the mandible and its insertion is the body of the hyoid bone. It protracts the hyoid bone.

GENIOGLOSSUS: a narrow muscle that is located dorsolateral to the geniohyoid

(Figure 3.4). It originates from the ventral surface of the mandible and inserts at the base of the tongue. The genioglossus moves the tongue during swallowing by pulling the tip of the tongue backward.

HYOGLOSSUS: a rhomboid-shaped muscle located lateral to the genioglossus (Figure 3.4). The Hypoglossal Nerve (CN XII) extends over its surface. The hyoglossus originates from the hyoid bone and inserts at the tongue, and it retracts and depresses the tongue.

STYLOGLOSSUS: a deep, narrow muscle that extends parallel to the digastric and lateral to the hyoglossus (Figure 3.4). Its origin is the mastoid process of the temporal bone, and it inserts at the base of the tongue. It retracts and elevates the tongue.

Muscles of the Head

The muscles of the head include superficial and deep muscles. The superficial muscles are mainly

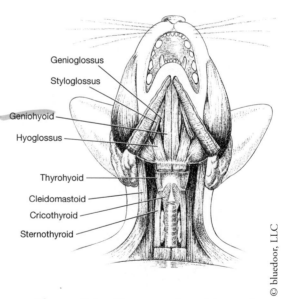

Genioglossus
Styloglossus
Geniohyoid
Hyoglossus
Thyrohyoid
Cleidomastoid
Cricothyroid
Sternothyroid

© bluedoor, LLC

Figure 3.4 – Deep muscles of the neck (ventral view).

involved in actions associated with facial expressions, and are derived from portions of the platysma. Since they are very difficult to identify in the cat, they will not be included in this study. Instead, we will focus attention on the two prominent muscles associated with moving the jaw. Clear away any remaining skin and connective tissue on one side of the head only to reveal the following muscles:

MASSETER: the prominent muscle of the jaw, it is located inferior and posterior to the eye to occupy much of the cheek area of the face (Figure 3.5). The masseter consists of three layers, each distinguishable by different fiber directions. However, due to the difficulty of separating these layers, do not dissect into the masseter. The masseter originates from the zygomatic arch and inserts at the mandible. Its primary action is elevation of the mandible.

TEMPORALIS: a large muscle occupying the temporal fossa on either side of the skull (Figure 3.5). Its origin is the temporal bone, and its insertion is the coronoid process of the mandible. It elevates the mandible.

MUSCLES OF THE UPPER LIMB

Muscles of the Shoulder

The muscles associated with the shoulder include eight major groups that provide movement of the brachium due to their insertions at the humerus. With your cat on its ventral side, transect and reflect the acromiotrapezius, spinotrapezius, and clavotrapezius muscles on one side, then identify the following shoulder muscles.

SUPRASPINATUS: a thick muscle that lies within the supraspinous fossa of the scapula (Figures 3.2 and 3.6), where it originates. The supraspinatus inserts at the greater tuberosity of the humerus. It protracts the humerus.

INFRASPINATUS: slightly smaller than the supraspinatus, it occupies the infraspinous fossa of the scapula (Figures 3.2 and 3.6). Its origin is the infraspinous fossa and its insertion is the lateral side of the greater tuberosity of the humerus. Its action is rotation of the humerus in a lateral direction.

TERES MAJOR: a thick, triangular muscle that extends along the axillary border of the scapula (Figures 3.2 and 3.6), from which it originates. With your probe, carefully separate this muscle

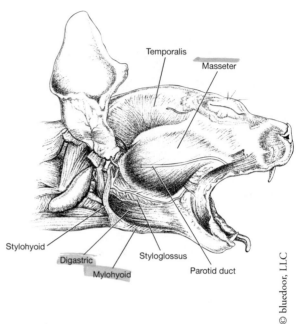

Figure 3.5 – Muscles of the head and neck (lateral view).

© bluedoor, LLC

from the infraspinatus. The teres major inserts at the proximal end of the humerus in common with a tendon associated with the latissimus dorsi. It flexes and rotates the humerus medially.

LEVATOR SCAPULAE VENTRALIS: a narrow muscle located between the clavotrapezius and acromiotrapezius muscles (Figure 3.2). It originates by way of two heads from the ventral side of the atlas bone and from the basioccipital bone. The two heads merge to form a flat band that inserts at the metacromion and into the infraspinous fossa of the scapula. It pulls the scapula in a cranial direction. *The levator scapulae ventralis is not present in humans.*

ACROMIODELTOID: a flat muscle located immediately ventral to the levator scapulae ventralis and caudal to the clavobrachialis (Figure 3.2). It originates from the acromion of the scapula and inserts at the spinodeltoid muscle. Its action is flexion and lateral rotation of the humerus. *The acromiodeltoid muscle is not a distinct muscle in the human, and instead contributes with the clavobrachialis and spinodeltoid of the cat to form the large deltoid on top of the shoulder.*

SPINODELTOID: a flat, band-shaped muscle located ventral to the acromiotrapezius and lev-

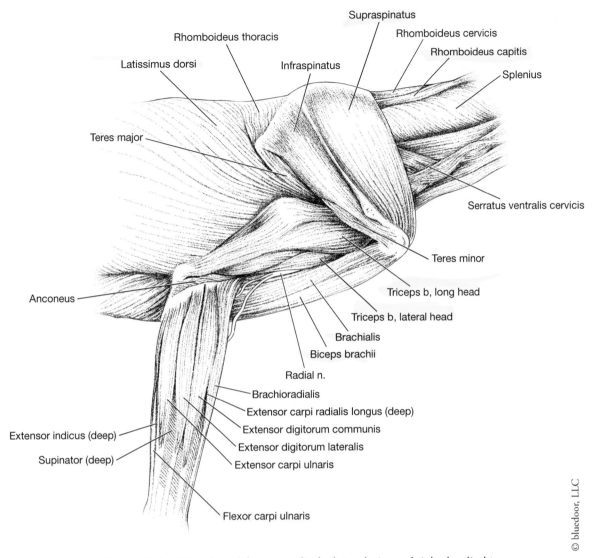

Supraspinatus

Rhomboideus thoracis

Rhomboideus cervicis

Rhomboideus capitis

Latissimus dorsi

Infraspinatus

Splenius

Teres major

Serratus ventralis cervicis

Teres minor

Anconeus

Triceps b, long head

Triceps b, lateral head

Brachialis

Biceps brachii

Radial n.

Brachioradialis

Extensor carpi radialis longus (deep)

Extensor digitorum communis

Extensor indicus (deep)

Extensor digitorum lateralis

Supinator (deep)

Extensor carpi ulnaris

Flexor carpi ulnaris

Figure 3.6 – Muscles of the upper limb (lateral view of right forelimb).

ator scapulae ventralis, and caudal to the acromiodeltoid (Figure 3.2). It originates from the spine of the scapula and inserts at the deltoid ridge of the humerus. It functions as a synergist with the acromiodeltoid to flex and rotate the humerus.

TERES MINOR: a small muscle located between the infraspinatus and the triceps brachii, it is deep to the spinodeltoid (Figure 3.6). To observe the teres minor, transect the spinodeltoid on one side and reflect it. The teres minor originates from the scapula near the glenoid fossa and inserts at the greater tuberosity of the humerus. It functions as a synergist with the

infraspinatus to laterally rotate the humerus.

SUBSCAPULARIS: a large, triangle-shaped muscle that occupies the subscapular fossa of the scapula (Figure 3.7), from which it originates. The subscapularis inserts at the dorsal border of the lesser tuberosity of the humerus. It adducts the humerus.

RHOMBOID GROUP: a group of three deep shoulder muscles that extends between thoracic vertebrae and the vertebral border of the scapula. To observe them, transect the clavotrapezius, levator scapulae ventralis, and acromiotrapezius muscles on one side of your cat and reflect the cut ends. Take care to avoid cutting too deeply and damaging the muscles that lie beneath.

RHOMBOIDEUS CAPITIS: the cranial muscle of the rhomboid group, it arises from fascia associated with the vertebral column, known as the **lambdoidal ridge** (Figure 3.6). From there, it forms a narrow, flat band that inserts at the cranial end of the vertebral border of the scapula. It rotates the scapula cranially.

RHOMBOIDEUS CERVICIS: the middle portion of the rhomboid group, it originates from the first four thoracic vertebrae and inserts at the middle vertebral border of the scapula (Figure 3.6). It adducts the scapula.

RHOMBOIDEUS THORACIS: the cranial rhomboid muscle. It arises from the first four thoracic vertebrae and inserts at the caudal end of the scapula's vertebral border (Figure 3.6). It adducts the scapula.

Muscles of the Brachium

The muscles of the upper arm, or brachium, move the humerus at the shoulder and the forearm at the elbow. They also serve to stabilize the shoulder during actions involving the forearm. With your cat on its ventral side, separate and identify the following muscles of the brachium.

CORACOBRACHIALIS: a short, narrow muscle located on the medial side of the shoulder. You can observe it where it nears the insertion of the subscapularis (Figure 3.7). The coracobrachialis originates from the coracoid process of the scapula and inserts at the proximal end of the humerus. It adducts the humerus.

EPITROCHLEARIS: a fragile, flat muscle on the medial surface of the brachium, it partially covers the large triceps brachii muscle (Figure 3.7). Its origin is from the lateral border of the latissimus dorsi and its insertion is by way of a thin aponeurosis that attaches to the olecranon process of the ulna. It functions as a synergist with the triceps brachii to extend the antebrachium. *The epitrochlearis is not present in the human.*

BICEPS BRACHII: a large, thick muscle located on the cranial surface of the humerus that acts as the primary flexor of the forearm (Figure 3.7). It originates from a tendon that attaches to the glenoid foss of the scapula, and inserts at the radial tuberosity. Its primary action is flexion of the antebrachium, but it also supinates the manus and stabilizes the shoulder joint. *The human biceps brachii includes two heads of origin, from which its name is derived: a short head at the glenoid fossa, and a long head at the coracoid process.*

TRICEPS BRACHII: a large, thick muscle that is mainly visible on the lateral side of the brachium, it is the primary extensor of the forearm (Figure 3.7). As its name suggests, it consists of three separate heads of origin: a **lateral head** from the deltoid ridge of the humerus; a **long head** from the axillary border of the scapula near the glenoid fossa; and a **medial head** from the medial side of the humerus. The medial head includes three parts, but do not attempt to separate them. All three heads unite to insert in common onto the olecranon process of the ulna. The primary action of the triceps brachii is extension of the antebrachium.

ANCONEUS: a small quadrangular muscle on the lateral surface of the elbow (Figure 3.6). It originates from the lateral epicondyle of the humerus and inserts at the lateral surface of the ulna. The anconeus functions as a synergist with the triceps brachii to extend the antebrachium.

BRACHIALIS: a small muscle on the craniolateral surface of the humerus, which is partially obscured by the lateral head of the triceps brachii (Figure 3.6). It originates from the lateral surface of the humerus and inserts at the lateral surface of the ulna near the semilunar notch. The brachialis functions as a synergist with the biceps brachii to flex the antebrachium.

Muscles of the Antebrachium and Manus

The muscles of the forearm, or antebrachium, act upon the carpus (wrist), manus (hand), and digits (fingers). They include a set of muscles on the dorsal side that work as extensors and muscles on the ventral side that function as flexors.

Notice that the antebrachium is covered with a two-layered sheet of connective tissue, which is known as the **antebrachial fascia**. In the carpal area, the fascia thickens to form a dorsal transverse ligament, the **extensor retinaculum**, and a ventral transverse ligament called the **flexor retinaculum** (Figure 3.7). The two ligaments support and anchor the tendons of the wrist area, then continue on to the manus.

Dissection of the antebrachium requires you to carefully remove the antebrachial fascia. To remove it, grasp both layers with your forceps and tug

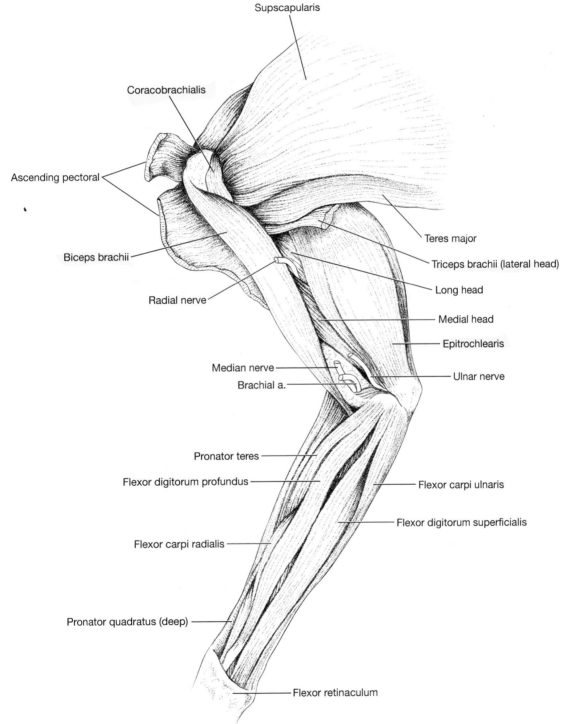

Supscapularis

Coracobrachialis

Ascending pectoral

Biceps brachii

Radial nerve

Teres major

Triceps brachii (lateral head)

Long head

Medial head

Epitrochlearis

Median nerve

Brachial a.

Ulnar nerve

Pronator teres

Flexor digitorum profundus

Flexor carpi ulnaris

Flexor digitorum superficialis

Flexor carpi radialis

Pronator quadratus (deep)

Flexor retinaculum

© bluedoor, LLC

Figure 3.7 – Muscles of the upper limb (medial view of right forelimb).

firmly, pulling it away from the underlying muscles. Use a scalpel to separate the deeper layer from the muscles, if necessary. Clean up the area until you can clearly observe the tendons on both the dorsal and ventral surfaces, since you will need to be able to trace the tendons of each muscle to their insertion.

With your cat on its ventral side, separate and identify the following muscles of the antebrachium, beginning with the dorsal superficial muscles.

BRACHIORADIALIS: a long, narrow muscle that is located on the cranial (radial) side of the dorsal antebrachium (Figure 3.6). It originates from the humerus about midway on the shaft, and inserts at the styloid process of the radius. Its action is supination of the manus.

EXTENSOR CARPI RADIALIS LONGUS: a narrow muscle located dorsal to the brachioradialis on the radial side of the antebrachium (Figure 3.6). Because it is deep to the brachioradialis, separate the two muscles and push aside the brachioradialis to view it. The extensor carpi radialis longus originates from the supracondyloid ridge of the humerus and inserts by way of a long tendon at the base of the second metacarpal. It extends the manus.

EXTENSOR CARPI RADIALIS BREVIS: located immediately medial to the extensor carpi radialis longus, it is slightly shorter than the neighboring muscle, as its name suggests (not shown). The extensor carpi radialis brevis originates from the supracondylar ridge of the humerus near the origin of the extensor carpi radialis brevis, and inserts at the base of the third metacarpal by way of a long tendon. It extends the manus.

EXTENSOR DIGITORUM COMMUNIS: a long, narrow muscle of the dorsal antebrachium that partially overlaps the extensor carpi radialis longus and brevis (Figure 3.6). Its origin is the supracondyloid ridge of the humerus near the origin of the extensor carpi radialis brevis, and it inserts by way of a long tendon that divides into four to attach to the three phalanges of the second through fifth digits. It extends the second through fifth digits of

the manus. *The human muscle is similar, although it is simply called the extensor digitorum.*

EXTENSOR DIGITORUM LATERALIS: a long, narrow muscle of the dorsal antebrachium located lateral to the extensor digitorum communis (Figure 3.6). It originates from the supracondyloid ridge of the humerus near the origin of the extensor digitorum communis, and inserts at a tendon that divides to attach to the phalanges of digits two through five. It extends the digits of the manus. *This dorsal muscle does not exist in the human, but is replaced by the extensor digiti minimi that inserts at the fifth digit to extend the little finger.*

EXTENSOR CARPI ULNARIS: a long, narrow muscle that extends along the ulnar side of the antebrachium (Figure 3.6). Its origin is from the lateral epicondyle of the humerus and it inserts at the base of the fifth metacarpal. The extensor carpi ulnaris is the last of the dorsal superficial muscles. It extends the carpals on the ulnar side.

SUPINATOR: a flat muscle that is located deep to the extensor digitorum communis and lateralis muscles, it covers the proximal end of the radius (Figure 3.6). The supinator originates from the lateral epicondyle of the humerus and inserts at the proximal one-third of the radius. It supinates the antebrachium.

ABDUCTOR POLLICIS LONGUS: a flat muscle located distal to the supinator, whose oblique fibers occupy the space between the radius and ulna (not shown). It originates from the dorsal surface of the radius and ventral surface of the ulna to insert at the first metacarpal. It extends and abducts digit 1 (the pollex, or thumb).

EXTENSOR INDICUS: with a probe, pull the extensor carpi ulnaris to one side to observe the extensor indicus beneath. It is a very narrow muscle that originates from the lateral surface of the ulna and inserts by blending in to the tendon of the extensor digitorum communis (Figure 3.6). It extends the first and second digits.

FLEXOR CARPI ULNARIS: a muscle with two heads of origin on the ventral side of the antebrachium (Figure 3.6). One head originates from the humerus near the medial epicondyle (called the humeral head), and the other head from the ulna at the olecranon (called the ulnar head). The heads converge to insert at the pisiform bone of the carpus. Its action is flexion of the carpus.

FLEXOR DIGITORUM SUPERFICIALIS: another flexor muscle of the ventral antebrachium arising from two heads of origin (Figure 3.7). One head is superficial, while the other is deep. The superficial head is a wide, prominent muscle arising from the coronoid process of the ulna, while the deep head arises from the medial epicondyle of the humerus and can be seen on the surface of the flexor digitorum profundus (to be described next). Both heads converge at the flexor retinaculum, then split to insert on either side of the middle phalanx of digits 2 through 5. It flexes the digits. *In the human, the palmaris longus is the equivalent muscle to the deep head of the flexor digitorum superficialis in the cat.*

FLEXOR DIGITORUM PROFUNDUS: located immediately ulnar to the large superficial head of the flexor digitorum superficialis on the ventral surface of the antebrachium (Figure 3.7). It extends deep from its origin along the radial border of the ulna, then divides into five tendons of insertion that attach to the distal phalanx of digits 1 through 5. It flexes all five digits.

FLEXOR CARPI RADIALIS: a narrow muscle that extends between the humerus and the manus and is located ulnar to the flexor digitorum profundus (Figure 3.7). It originates from the medial epicondyle of the humerus and inserts at the second and third metacarpals. Its action is flexion of the carpus.

PRONATOR TERES: a muscle with oblique fibers that extend over the ventral surface of the antebrachium (Figure 3.7). It originates from the medial epicondyle of the humerus and inserts at the medial border of the radius. It pronates the manus by rotating the radius. *There are two heads of origin in the pronator teres of the human, a humeral head and an ulnar head.*

PRONATOR QUADRATUS: a deep ventral muscle of the antebrachium with oblique fibers extending between the distal ends of the ulna and radius (Figure 3.7). To observe this muscle, separate the flexor digitorum profundus and the flexor carpi radialis. The pronator quadratus lies deep between the two, covered with a thin fascia. It functions as a synergist with the pronator teres to rotate the radius to produce pronation of the manus.

MUSCLES OF THE LOWER LIMB

Muscles of the Thigh

The muscles of the thigh provide movement to the femur at the hip joint, and to the foreleg, or shank, at the knee joint. They include some of the thickest muscles of the cat, providing it with its abilities to leap and run. In this section, you will begin by identifying the superficial muscles of the thigh, beginning with the medial side and working to the lateral side. Once the superficial muscles have been observed, you will then transect and reflect them to observe the deep thigh muscles on both sides.

SARTORIUS: with your cat on its dorsal side, identify the sartorius as the flat, thin muscle on the cranial aspect of the medial side of the thigh (Figure 3.8). It originates from the iliac crest to extend down the thigh on the medial side to finally insert at the fascia surrounding the knee and the tibia. The actions of the sartorius include adduction and rotation of the femur, and extension of the shank. Separate this muscle, then transect it on one side. *The human sartorius is a long, narrow band that extends from its origin at the iliac spine to insert at the tibia.*

GRACILIS: a flat, thin muscle that fills the caudal aspect of the medial thigh (Figure 3.8). The gracilis originates from the ischium and pubis, and inserts at a thin aponeurosis that is continuous with the fascia associated with the shank. It adducts and retracts the thigh. After cleaning the fat and connective tissue from the gracilis, transect it on the same side as the sartorius.

TENSOR FASCIA LATAE: a triangle-shaped muscle that covers most of the cranial surface of the thigh and borders the sartorius (Figure 3.9). It originates from the ventral border of the ilium and fascia of nearby hip muscles. Its insertion is by way of a prominent fascia called the **fascia lata**, which continues from the muscle distally to insert at the surface of the patella. Contraction tightens the fascia lata, which helps to extend the shank. Use caution to separate this muscle, taking care to avoid damaging the fascia lata and the muscles that lie beneath it.

BICEPS FEMORIS: turn your cat over onto its ventral side and notice the large, thick muscle that dominates the lateral surface of the thigh (Figure 3.9). The biceps femoris originates from one head in the cat, the ischial tuberosity, and inserts at the proximal one-third of the tibia and the lateral side of the patella. It abducts the thigh and flexes the shank. *The name biceps means "two heads", and refers to the origin of this muscle from two heads in the human, from which the term was first applied. The human biceps femoris includes a long head from the ischial tuberosity and a short head from the linea aspera of the femur.* Separate this muscle carefully in order to avoid damaging the fragile muscle that lies deep, called the tenuissimus, and the sciatic nerve that extends immediately deep as a long, white string. Once you've separated it, transect it on one side.

TENUISSIMUS: an extremely thin, narrow muscle immediately deep to the biceps femoris, and often adheres to it (Figure 3.10). It originates from the second caudal vertebra and inserts at the tibia in common with the biceps femoris. It functions as a synergist with the biceps femoris to abduct the thigh and flex the shank. *The tenuissimus is not present in humans.*

CAUDOFEMORALIS: a thick muscle located immediately cranial to the biceps femoris and extending beneath it (Figure 3.10). The caudofemoralis originates from the second and third caudal vertebrae and inserts at the lateral border of the patella by way of a thin tendon. It abducts the thigh and flexes the shank. *The caudofemoralis is not present in humans.*

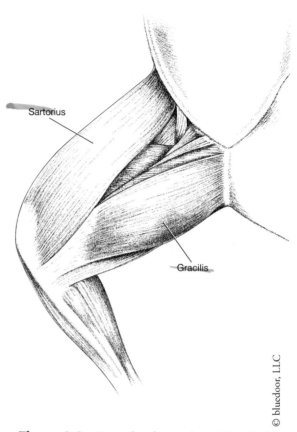

Figure 3.8 – Superficial muscles of the thigh (ventral view).

© bluedoor, LLC

SEMITENDINOSUS: a long muscle occupying the caudal border of the thigh, and visible from both the medial and lateral aspects (Figure 3.10). It originates from the ischial tuberosity and inserts at the medial surface of the tibia. It flexes the shank.

SEMIMEMBRANOSUS: located cranial to the more narrow semitendinosus, it can be observed on the medial aspect of the thigh or from the lateral aspect of the thigh beneath the rectus femoris (Figure 3.11). The semimembranosus originates from the tuberosity and ramus of the ischium, and inserts at the medial epicondyle at the distal end of the femur. It extends the thigh. *In the human, the thick semimembranosus inserts at the medial condyle of the tibia.*

ADDUCTOR FEMORIS: a deep muscle of the lateral thigh that is cranial to the semimembra-

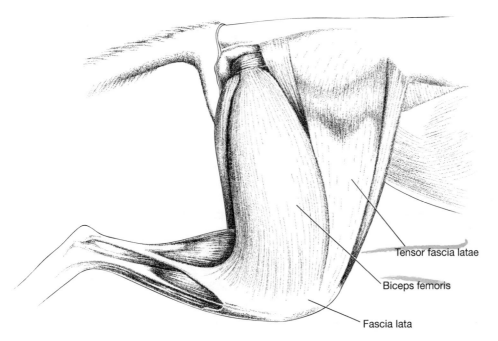

© bluedoor, LLC

Tensor fascia latae

Biceps femoris

Fascia lata

Figure 3.9 – Superficial muscles of the thigh (lateral view).

nosus, with which it is partially covered. Reflect the biceps femoris in order to observe the adductor femoris, which originates from the rami of the pubis and ischium and inserts at the lower one-third of the femur (Figure 3.11). It adducts the thigh. *This muscle is called the adductor magnus in the human.*

ADDUCTOR LONGUS: a thin, triangle-shaped muscle located cranial to the adductor femoris (Figure 3.11). It originates from the craniomedial border of the pubis and inserts at the linea aspera in the middle portion of the femur. Its action is adduction of the thigh.

PECTINEUS: a small, triangle-shaped muscle cranial to the adductor longus beneath the femoral blood vessels and the saphenous nerve (Figure 3.11). The pectineus originates from the cranial border of the pubis and inserts at the shaft of the femur. It adducts the thigh.

QUADRICEPS GROUP: a complex of four powerful muscles on the cranial aspect of the thigh, which share a common tendon of insertion that wraps around the knee to attach to the tibial tuberosity. Together, these four muscles provide force to extend the shank at the knee joint. Separate and identify the following:

VASTUS MEDIALIS: the most medial of the four muscles of the quadriceps complex, it originates from the shaft of the femur (Figure 3.11).

RECTUS FEMORIS: covered by a shiny layer of fascia, it is sandwiched between the vastus medialis and vastus lateralis to occupy the cranial surface of the thigh (Figure 3.11). It originates from the ilium near the acetabulum.

VASTUS LATERALIS: a large flat muscle lateral to the rectus femoris, it originates from the greater trochanter and shaft of the femur (Figure 3.10).

VASTUS INTERMEDIUS: located deep to the rectus femoris, observe it by separating the rectus femoris and vastus lateralis carefully without cutting (not shown). It originates from the shaft of the femur along most of its length.

ILIOPSOAS GROUP: two muscles that are mostly obscured by abdominal muscles in the cranial hip region on the ventral aspect of the cat. Do not dissect to observe them at this time, but rather refer to Figure 3.12. You will be able to observe the iliacus, psoas major, and psoas minor muscles when you open the abdominal cavity. The two muscles of the iliopsoas group insert by a common tendon at the lesser

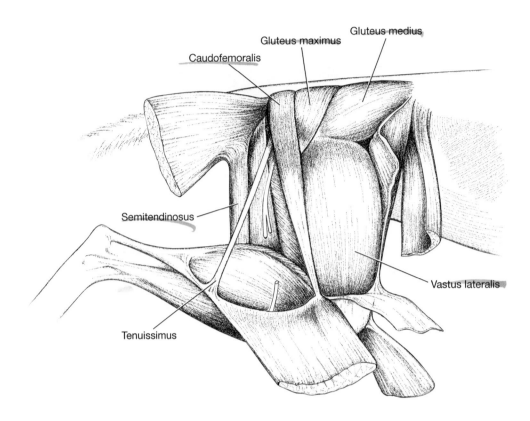

Caudofemoralis

Gluteus maximus

Gluteus medius

Semitendinosus

Vastus lateralis

Tenuissimus

Figure 3.10 – Deep muscles of the thigh (lateral view).

trochanter of the femur to flex and rotate the thigh.

ILIACUS: the lateral of the two muscles forming the iliopsoas group, it originates from the ventral border of the ilium.

PSOAS MAJOR: located medial to the iliacus, it originates from the last thoracic and each of the lumbar vertebrae.

PSOAS MINOR: a thin muscle medial to the psoas major. It originates from the last thoracic and first three lumbar vertebrae and inserts at the pubis by way of a long tendon. It flexes the pelvis toward the abdomen.

Muscles of the Shank and Pes

The muscles of the foreleg, or shank, act upon the tarsus (ankle) to provide movement of the foot, or pes. Some also participate in movement of the shank at the knee joint. The shank muscles are bound by a tough outer fascia, which must be removed to identify them. To remove the shank fascia, cut it with scissors or a scalpel and pull it

firmly away from the muscle layer. While performing this procedure, be careful to avoid damaging the tendons of insertion. Notice the transverse band of fascia that holds the cranial muscle tendons in place, which is called the **extensor retinaculum**.

Similar to the muscles of the antebrachium, the shank muscles include extensors and flexors. With your cat on its dorsal side, you will identify the flexors first, which are located on the cranial aspect of the shank.

TIBIALIS CRANIALIS: a large, flat muscle dominating the craniolateral aspect of the tibia (Figure 3.13). It originates from the proximal end of the tibia and fibula, and its tendon of insertion extends beneath the extensor retinaculum to the first metatarsal. Its action is flexion of the pes.

EXTENSOR DIGITORUM LONGUS: a long, prominent muscle located deep to the tibialis cranialis (Figure 3.13). To observe it, separate it from the tibialis cranialis. The extensor digitorum longus originates from the lateral epicondyle of the femur. Its tendon of insertion extends beneath the extensor retinaculum, then divides into four that attach to the second and third phalanges of digits 2-5. It extends the digits.

EXTENSOR HALLUCIS LONGUS: a deep muscle beneath the tibialis cranialis and extensor digitorum longus (Figure 3.13). Due to its small size, do not dissect to observe it. It originates from the anterior surface of the fibula and inserts on the first metatarsal. Its action is flexion of the pes.

PERONEUS LONGUS: one of three peroneus muscles on the lateral side of the shank, it is the most superficial of the three (Figure 3.14). It originates from the lateral surface of the fibula and inserts at the proximal ends of all five metatarsals, and its action is flexion of the pes.

PERONEUS TERTIUS: a narrow muscle located deep to the peroneus longus (Figure 3.14). It

originates from the lateral surface of the fibula and inserts at the first phalanx of the fifth digit. It flexes the pes, and abducts and extends the fifth digit. Follow its tendon of insertion and note that it passes within a groove of the lateral malleolus.

PERONEUS BREVIS: the smallest of the peroneus muscles, it is located caudal to the peroneus longus and tertius (Figure 3.14). It originates from the distal one-half of the fibula and inserts in common with the tendon of the peroneus tertius. It flexes the pes.

POPLITEUS: a small triangle-shaped muscle extending obliquely across the dorsal aspect of the knee from the femur to the tibia (Figure 3.14). The popliteus originates from the lateral epicondyle of the femur and inserts at the proximal end of the tibia. It flexes and medially rotates the shank.

FLEXOR DIGITORUM LONGUS: a long, narrow muscle located posterior to the tibia on the

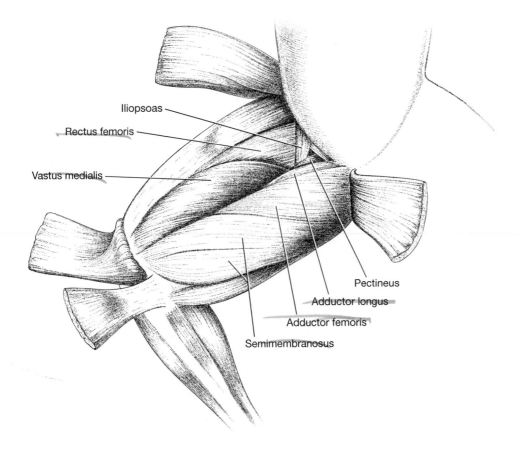

Figure 3.11 – Deep muscles of the thigh (ventral view).

Iliopsoas
Rectus femoris
Vastus medialis
Pectineus
Adductor longus
Adductor femoris
Semimembranosus

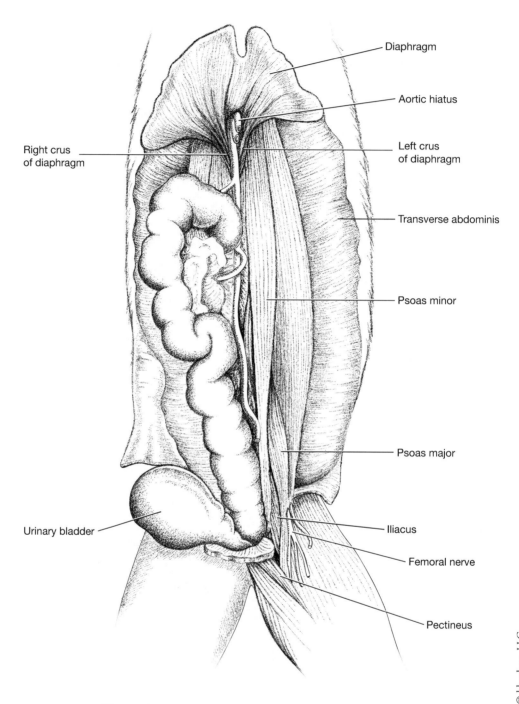

Diaphragm

Aortic hiatus

Right crus
of diaphragm

Left crus
of diaphragm

Transverse abdominis

Psoas minor

Psoas major

Urinary bladder

Iliacus

Femoral nerve

Pectineus

© bluedoor, LLC

Figure 3.12 – Deep muscles of the lumbar region
(ventral view of opened abdominopelvic cavity).

medial side of the shank (Figure 3.14). It originates from the head of the fibula and shaft of
the tibia. The tendon of insertion begins as a
broad tendon that extends over the plantar surface of the foot, then divides into four narrow
tendons that insert at the terminal phalanx of
digits 2 through 5. It flexes the pes and digits.

FLEXOR HALUUCIS LONGUS: slightly larger
than the flexor digitorum longus, it is located
lateral to it on the dorsal aspect of the shank
(Figure 3.14). The flexor hallucis longus originates from the shafts of both the tibia and
fibula, and inserts at the base of the phalanx of
the first digit. It flexes the pes and digits.

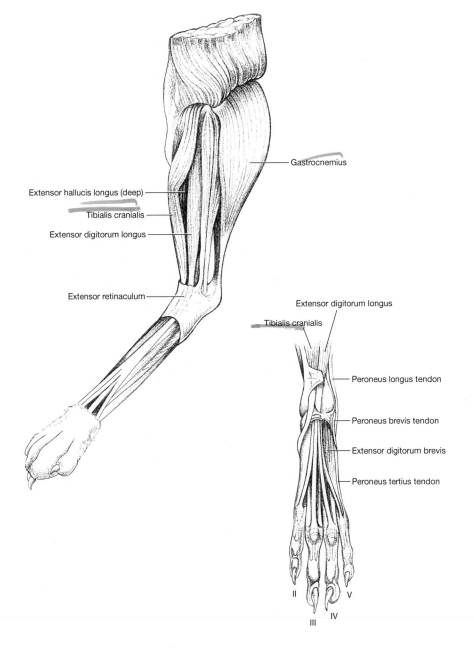

Gastrocnemius

Extensor hallucis longus (deep)

Tibialis cranialis

Extensor digitorum longus

Extensor retinaculum

Extensor digitorum longus

Tibialis cranialis

Peroneus longus tendon

Peroneus brevis tendon

Extensor digitorum brevis

Peroneus tertius tendon

II

V

IV

III

© bluedoor, LLC

Figure 3.13 – Muscles of the shank and pes (dorsal view of left hindlimb).

GASTROCNEMIUS: the largest muscle on the dorsal side of the shank, it forms most of the bulk commonly known as the calf muscle (Figures 3.13 and 3.14). It includes two heads of origin, a lateral and a medial head. The lateral head originates from the patella, the fascia of the shank, a small sesamoid bone located cranial to the lateral epicondyle of the femur, and an aponeurosis from the plantaris and nearby tibia. The medial head arises from the sesamoid bone and the shaft of the femur. The gastrocnemius inserts by way of a large, thick tendon called the **calcaneus tendon** (commonly referred to as the Achilles tendon) that

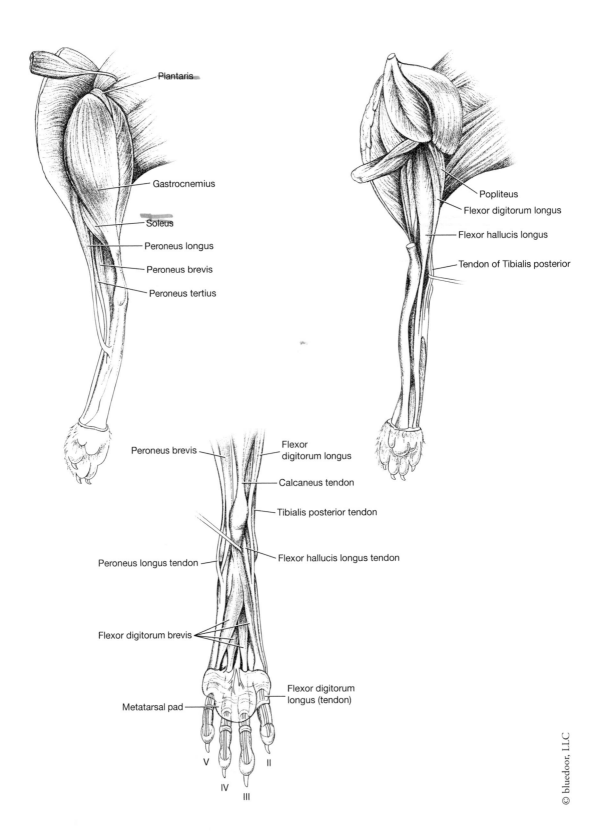

Figure 3.14 – Muscles of the shank and pes (dorsal view of left hindlimb).

attaches to the proximal end of the calcaneus bone. The gastrocnemius extends the pes and flexes the antebrachium.

PLANTARIS: a broad, somewhat flat muscle that is located deep to the gastrocnemius (Figure 3.14). You can observe it protruding between the two heads of the gastrocnemius. Carefully separate the plantaris from the two heads of the gastrocnemius, then trace its origin from the sesamoid bone near the lateral epicondyle of the femur to its insertion in common with the calcaneus tendon. The plantaris acts as a synergist with the gastrocnemius to extend the pes.

SOLEUS: a flat muscle located deep to the plantaris (Figure 3.14). It arises from the proximal one-third of the fibula and inserts in common with the calcaneus tendon. Similar to the plantaris, it acts as a synergist with the gastrocnemius to extend the pes.

EXTENSOR DIGITORUM BREVIS: a thin, narrow muscle that covers the dorsolateral surface of the tarsus and metatarsus (Figure 3.13). It originates from metatarsals 3 through 5. Its tendon of insertion splits into three distinct tendons, all of which attach to the first phalanx. Its action is extension of the toes.

FLEXOR DIGITORUM BREVIS: a small muscle on the plantar surface of the pes (Figure 3.14). It originates from the calcaneus tendon and its insertion splits into three tendons that insert at the second phalanx of digits 2 through 5. It flexes the toes.

Muscles of the Hip

The muscles of the hip include the gluteal complex and the deeper pelvic muscles on the dorsal side. They act upon the hip joint to move the thigh. With your cat on its ventral side, carefully remove the tough fascia covering the hip region by cutting through it with scissors or scalpel and pulling it away with forceps. Notice the tensor fascia latae, caudofemoralis, and biceps femoris identified previously, then separate and identify the following muscles of the hip.

GLUTEUS MAXIMUS: a thick, short muscle located cranial to the caudofemoralis (Figure 3.10). It originates from the transverse processes of the last sacral and first caudal vertebrae, and inserts at the greater trochanter of the femur. Contraction of the gluteus maximus abducts the thigh. After separating this muscle, transect it on one side with care to avoid cutting the deeper muscles, and reflect the cut ends. *In humans, the gluteus maximus arises from the iliac crest, lower sacrum, and coccyx and inserts at the fascia lata and shaft of the femur. It is a much more extensive muscle than the g. maximus of quadripeds, due to the stepping motion required of the bipedal gait.*

GLUTEUS MEDIUS: a thick muscle located between the cranial end of the tensor fascia latae and the caudal end of the gluteus maximus (Figure 3.10). It arises from the iliac crest, last sacral vertebrae, first caudal vertebrae, and the fascia lata. Its insertion is at the greater trochanter of the femur. It abducts the thigh. After separating the gluteus medius, transect it on one side with care to avoid cutting the deeper muscles, and reflect the cut ends. *The g. medius is larger than the g. maximus in the cat and other quadripeds, but smaller that the g. maximus in humans.*

PIRIFORMIS: a triangle-shaped muscle located deep to the gluteus medius (Figure 3.15). Note the thin, string-like sciatic nerve that passes under the piriformis. It arises from the transverse processes of the last two sacral and first caudal vertebrae, and inserts at the greater trochanter of the femur. The piriformis abducts the thigh. After separating this muscle, transect it on one side and reflect the cut ends. Take care to avoid cutting the sciatic nerve as you perform this procedure.

GLUTEUS MINIMUS: located deep to the gluteus medius and cranial to the piriformis, it includes a cranial narrow bundle and a caudal triangle-shaped bundle (Figure 3.15). The gluteus minimus arises from the lateral surface of the ilium and inserts at the greater trochanter of the femur. It abducts the thigh and rotates it medially.

GEMELLUS CRANIALIS: a small, triangle-shaped muscle located caudal to the piriformis and bordering the caudal rim of the gluteus minimus (Figure 3.15). It originates from the dorsal border of the ischium and ilium, and inserts at the greater trochanter of the femur. It abducts and medially rotates the thigh. *Known as the gemellus superior in the human, it arises from the ischial spine and rotates the thigh in a lateral direction.*

GEMELLUS CAUDALIS: a small, flat muscle located caudal to the gemellus cranialis (Figure 3.15). It arises from the dorsolateral surface of the ischium and inserts into the trochanteric fossa of the femur. It abducts the thigh. *Known as the gemellus inferior in the human, it rotates the thigh in a lateral direction.*

OBTURATOR INTERNUS: located caudal to the gemellus cranialis (Figure 3.15). It originates from the ramus of the ischium and inserts at the trochanteric fossa in common with the gemellus caudalis. It abducts the thigh.

OBTURATOR EXTERNUS: a deep muscle located adjacent to the gemellus caudalis, it arises from the pubis and ischium near the border of the obturator foramen and inserts into the trochanteric fossa of the femur (not shown). It laterally rotates and retracts the thigh.

QUADRATUS FEMORIS: a short, thick muscle of the hip that originates from the ischial tuberosity and inserts along the ventral borders of the greater and lesser trochanters (Figure 3.15). It laterally rotates the thigh.

DEEP MUSCLES OF THE TRUNK

Deep Thoracic Muscles

With your cat still on its dorsal side, you will now identify the muscles that lie deep to the pectoralis muscle group. To view them, transect and reflect the pectoralis major, pectoralis minor, and xiphihumeralis muscles on one side.

SERRATUS VENTRALIS: a large, fan-shaped muscle extending between the thorax and the scapula (Figures 3.1 and 3.16). It originates from the first nine or ten ribs and last five cervical vertebrae, and inserts at the vertebral border of the scapula. Its contraction draws the scapula toward the thoracic wall. *This muscle is represented as two distinct muscles in the human: an anterior **levator scapulae**, which originates from the cervical vertebrae, and a posterior **serratus anterior**, originating from the ribs.*

SCALENUS: a group of three narrow muscles, from cranial to caudal, known as the **scalenus anterior**, **scalenus medius**, and **scalenus posterior** (Figure 3.1). They originate from different locations at the ribs, but converge at their cranial ends to form a single bundle that inserts at the transverse processes of the cervical vertebrae. Together, they pull the ribs cranially to expand the thorax.

TRANSVERSE COSTARUM: a thin, narrow muscle that covers the cranial portion of the rectus abdominis muscle (Figure 3.1). It originates from the sternum to insert at the first rib and costal cartilage, and its action pulls the ribs cranially.

EXTERNAL INTERCOSTALS: the outer layer of small, thin muscles that extend between adjacent ribs to cover the intercostal spaces from the seventh rib to the thirteenth rib (Figure 3.16). The external intercostals run in a craniodorsal direction, similar to the external oblique muscle of the abdomen. They originate from a cranial rib (starting at the seventh rib) and insert at an adjacent caudal rib. Their action is protraction of the ribs, which is required for inspiration (inhaling air).

INTERNAL INTERCOSTALS: the inner (deep) layer of small muscles between the ribs (Figure 3.16). Their fibers extend in a caudodorsal direction, similar to the internal oblique. They originate from a caudal rib to insert at an adjacent cranial rib, and their action is retraction of the ribs to produce forced expiration.

TRANSVERSE THORACIS: a third layer that lies deep to the internal intercostals (not shown). It represents a thoracic continuation of the transverse abdominis muscle, and is best seen during dissection of the thoracic cavity. Its origin is the dorsolateral border of the sternum from the third to the eighth rib, and it inserts at the costal cartilages of the same ribs. The transverse thoracis muscle draws the ribs downward.

SERRATUS DORSALIS CRANIALIS: a thin muscle that extends along the dorsal part of the thoracic wall and neck beneath the latissimus dorsi (Figure 3.16). Its origin is from the fascia along the middorsal line and inserts at the first nine ribs. It draws the ribs in a cranial direction.

SERRATUS DORSALIS CAUDALIS: a thin muscle extending from the cranial border of the serratus dorsalis cranialis to the lumbar region (Figure 3.16). Notice that the fibers of the serratus dorsalis cranialis and caudalis run in directions opposite to one another. The serratus dorsalis caudalis originates from the middorsal fascia and inserts at the last four or five ribs. Its action is to draw the ribs in a caudal direction. *In the human, the serratus posterior superior is associated only with ribs two through five, and the serratus posterior inferior with the lower four ribs.*

Deep Muscles of the Back

The deep muscles of the back extend the vertebral column. To view them, first find the large sheet of fascia extending from the middle to the caudal back, known as the **lumbodorsal fascia**. Separate

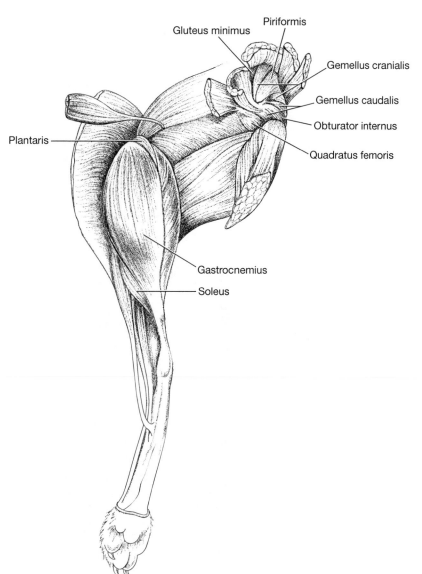

Figure 3.15 – Deep muscles of the hip (dorsal view of left hindlimb).

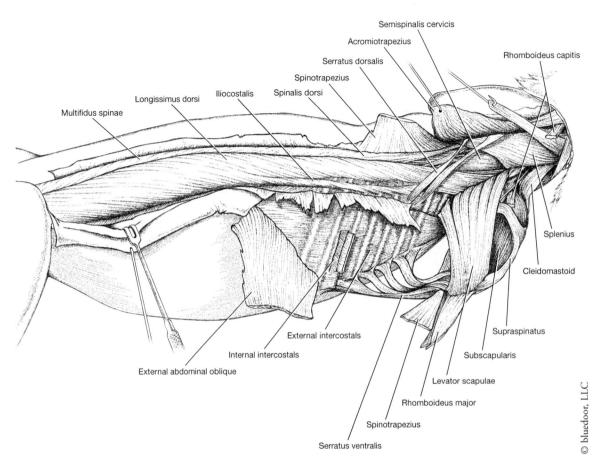

Figure 3.16 – Deep muscles of the trunk (dorsolateral view).

the lumbodorsal fascia by grasping it with forceps and pulling it away from underlying muscles, then making a small "window" through the fascia by cutting a three-sided hole roughly two inches on each side. By opening your "window," you will be able to observe the deep back muscles. We will begin studying the deep muscles of the back at the caudal end of the cat.

MULTIFIDUS SPINAE: an extensive muscle of the lumbar region of the back that consists of numerous bundles of fibers (Figure 3.16). The fibers appear to submerge at the vertebral column. The muscle bundles forming the multifidus originate from the thoracic and lumbar vertebrae and sacrum, and insert at the more cranial vertebrae. When both sides contract at the same time, the vertebral column is extended. When one side contracts, the vertebral column bends toward that side.

LONGISSIMUS DORSI: an extensive back muscle that includes large bundles, each extending from the lumbar region of the back to gradually become less prominent in the thoracic and cervical regions (not shown). The bundles are the medial and lateral bundles, with the lateral bundle further separated by fascia into upper and lower portions. The medial bundle originates from the neural spines of vertebrae, and the lateral bundle originates from the neural spines and from the ilium. The bundles insert at more cranial vertebrae at various processes. The longissimus dorsi extends the vertebral column. *The human longissimus dorsi is similar, except its bundles are called the longissimus cervicis and longissimus thoracis and include a third bundle, the longissimus capitis. The longissimus capitis is a separate muscle in the cat, associated with the neck region.*

SPINALIS DORSI: a deep back muscle in the thoracic region, which can be identified as a medial separation from the longissimus dorsi (Figure 3.16). It originates from the neural spines of the more caudal thoracic vertebra and inserts at the transverse processes of the more cranial vertebrae. The action is extension of the vertebral column. *The human spinalis is more extensive, and is divided into a spinalis capitis, spinalis cervicis, and spinalis thoracis.*

ILIOCOSTALIS: a thin muscle of the deep back in the thoracic region (Figure 3.16). It consists of a number of small bundles lateral to the longissimus dorsi. The iliocostalis originates from the lateral surface of the ribs and inserts at the lateral surface of most cranial ribs. Its action pulls the ribs together. *Similar to the spinalis, the iliocostalis is more extensive in humans. It extends from the neck region to the iliac crest and includes cervicis, thoracis, and lumborum groups.*

SPLENIUS: a large, flat muscle on the dorsolateral side of the cranial back and neck, located deep to the rhomoideus capitis (Figure 3.16). It arises from the fascia along the middorsal line of the neck and inserts at the lambdoidal ridge of the occipital bone. Contraction of the splenius flexes the head laterally. *In the human, the splenius includes two distinct origins and insertions: the splenius capitis arises from the seventh cervical and upper three thoracic vertebrae to insert at the mastoid process of the temporal bone, and the splenius cervicis extends from the third through 6th thoracic vertebrae to the upper 2 or 3 cervical vertebrae.*

LONGISSIMUS CAPITIS: a narrow muscle that is a cranial continuation of the longissimus dorsi and borders the ventral edge of the splenius. It arises from cervical vertebrae 4 through 7, and inserts at the mastoid process of the temporal bone. Its action is lateral flexion of the head.

SEMISPINALIS CERVICIS: a muscle deep to the splenius. To observe it, transect the splenius at right angles to its fibers and reflect the cut ends. The semispinalis cervicis extends from the seventh cervical and first three thoracic vertebrae to insert at the lambdoidal crest of the occipital bone. Its action is elevation of the head.

SEMISPINALIS CAPITIS: also deep to the splenius, a flat muscle that arises from cervical vertebrae 3-7 and the first three thoracic vertebrae. It inserts at the lambdoidal crest of the occipital bone, and its action is elevation of the head.

Table 3.1 – The origins, insertions, and primary actions of the muscles of the cat.

MUSCLE	ORIGIN	INSERTION	ACTION
abductor pollicis longus	dorsal surface of the radius and ventral surface of the ulna	first metacarpal	extends and abducts digit 1
acromiodeltoid	acromion of the scapula	spinodeltoid muscle	flexion and lateral rotation of the humerus
acromiotrapezius	middorsal line from the spine of the axis to the fourth thoracic vertebra	metacromion and spine of the scapula	adducts the scapula
adductor femoris	rami of the pubis and ischium	lower one-third of the femur	adducts the thigh
adductor longus	craniomedial border of the pubis	linea aspera of middle femur	adducts the thigh
anconeus	lateral epicondyle of the humerus	lateral surface of the ulna	extends the antebrachium
biceps brachii	glenoid foss of the scapula	radial tuberosity	flexes the antebrachium, supinates the manus, and stabilizes the shoulder joint
biceps femoris	proximal one-third of the tibia and the lateral side of the patella	ischial tuberosity	abducts the thigh and flexes the shank
brachialis	lateral surface of the humers	lateral surface of the ulna near the semilunar notch	flexes the antebrachium
brachioradialis	the humerus about midway on the shaft	styloid process of the radius	supination of the manus
caudofemoralis	second and third caudal verebrae	lateral border of patella	abducts the thigh and flexes the shank
clavobrachialis	clavicle	lateral surface of the ulna near the semilunar notch	flexes the antebrachium
clavotrapezius	middorsal fascia of the 7th cervical vertebrae	clavicle	forward extension of the humerus
cleidomastoid	mastoid process of the temporal bone	clavicle	rotates the head when the clavicle is held stationary, and moves the clavicle cranially when the head is held stationary
cricothyroid	cricoid cartilage of the larynx	thyroid cartilage	regulates the tension exerted on the vocal chords
digastric	mastoid and jugular processes of the temporal	medial ventral border of the mandible	depression of the mandible
epitrochlearis	lateral border of the latissimus dorsi	thin aponeurosis that attaches to the olecranon	extends the antebrachium
extensor carpi radialis longus	supracondyloid ridge of the humerus	base of the third metacarpal	extends the manus

extensor carpi ulnaris	lateral epicondyle of the humerus	base of fifth metacarpal	extends the carpals on the ulnar side
extensor digitorum communis	supracondyloid ridge of the humerus	three phalanges of the second through fifth digits	extends the second through fifth digits
extensor digitorum lateralis	supracondyloid ridge of the humerus	phalanges of digits two through five	extends the digits of the manus
extensor indicus	lateral surface of the ulna	three phalanges of the second through fifth digits	extends first and second digits of the manus
extensor digitorum longus	lateral epicondyle of the femur	second and third phalanges of digits 2-5	extends the digits of the pes
extensor hallucis longus	anterior surface of the fibula	first metatarsal	flexion of the pes
extensor digitorum brevis	metatarsals 3 through 5	a single tendon splits into three distinct tendons, all of which attach to the first phalanx of the pes	extension of the digits of the pes
external intercostals	from a cranial rib starting at the seventh	adjacent caudal rib	protraction of the ribs
external oblique	lumbodorsal fascia of the caudal ribs	sternum and along the linea alba	compresses the abdomen
flexor carpi radialis	medial epicondyle of the humerus	second and third metacarpals	flexion of the carpus
flexor carpi ulnaris	two heads: humeral head near the medial epicondyle of the humerus; ulnar head from the ulna at the olecranon	pisiform bone of the carpus	flexion of the carpus
flexor digitorum brevis	calcaneus tendon	splits into three tendons that insert at the second phalanx of digits 2-5	flexes the digits of the pes
flexor digitorum longus	head of the fibula and shaft of the tibia	divides into four narrow tendons that insert at the terminal phalanx of digits 2 through 5	flexes the pes and digits
flexor digitorum profundus	radial border of the ulna	divides into five tendons that attach to the distal phalanx of digits 1 through 5	flexes the digits of the manus
flexor digitorum superficialis	two heads: superficial head from the coronoid process of the ulna; deep head from the medial epicondyle of the humerus	either side of the middle phalanx of digits 2 through 5	flexes the digits of the manus
flexor hallucis longus	shafts of both the tibia and fibula	distal phalanx of first digit	flexes the pes and digits

gastrocnemius	two heads: lateral head from the patella, the fascia of the shank, a sesamoid bone located cranial to the lateral epicondyle of the femur, and an aponeurosis from the plantaris and nearby tibia; medial head from the sesamoid bone and the shaft of the femur	calcaneus	extends the pes and flexes the antebrachium
gemellus caudalis	dorsolateral surface of the ischium	trochanteric fossa of the femur	abducts the thigh
gemellus cranialis	dorsal border of the ischium and ilium	greater trochanter of the femus	abducts and medially rotates the thigh
genioglossus	ventral surface of the mandible	base of the tongue	moves the tongue during swallowing by pulling the tip of the tongue backward
geniohyoid	ventral surface of the mandible	body of the hyoid bone	protracts the hyoid bone
gluteus maximus	transverse processes of the last sacral and first caudal vertebrae	greater trochanter of the femur	abducts the thigh
gluteus medius	iliac crest, last sacral vertebrae, first caudal vertebrae, and the fascia lata	greater trochanter of the femur	abducts the thigh
gluteus minimus	lateral surface of the ilium	greater trochanter of the femur	abducts the thigh and rotates it medially
gracilis	ischium and pubis	at a thin aponeurosis that is continuous with the fascia associated with the shank	adducts and retracts the thigh
hyoglossus	hyoid bone	base of the tongue	retracts and depresses the tongue
infraspinatus	infraspinous fossa	lateral side of the greater tuberosity of the humerus	lateral rotation of the humerus
iliacus	ventral border of the ilium	lesser trochanter of the femur	flex and rotate the thigh
iliocostalis	lateral surface of most caudal ribs	lateral surface of most cranial ribs	pulls the ribs together to compress the thorax
internal intercostal	caudal rib	cranial rib	retraction of the ribs
internal oblique	lumbodorsal fascia of the caudal ribs	sternum and along the linea alba	compresses the abdomen
latissimus dorsi	fourth or fifth thoracic vertebrae to the sixth lumbar vertebra	medial surface of the humerus	pulls the forelimb dorsocaudally
levator scapulae ventralis	two heads: from the ventral side of the atlas bone and from the basioccipital bone	metacromion and into the infraspinous fossa of the scapula	pulls the scapula cranially

longissimus capitis	cervical vertebrae 4 through 7	the mastoid process of the temporal bone	lateral flexion of the head
masseter	zygomatic arch	ramus of the mandible	elevates the mandible
multifidus spinae	thoracic and lumbar vertebrae and sacrum	cranial vertebrae	both sides contract at the same time, the vertebral column is extended; one side contracts, the vertebral column bends toward that side
mylohyoid	medial surface of the mandible	median raphe	elevates the floor of the mouth
obturator externus	pubis and ischium near the border of the obturator foramen	trochanteric fossa of the femur	laterally rotates and retracts the thigh
obturator internus	ramus of the ischium	trochanteric fossa	abducts the thigh
pectineus	cranial border of the pubis	shaft of the femur	adducts the thigh
pectoantebrachialis	ventral midline	proximal end of the humerus	adduction of the humerus
pectoralis major	two heads: superficial head from the ventral midline and manubrium; deep head from the cranial half of the sternum	proximal third of the humerus	adduction of the humerus
pectoralis minor	six sternebrae or the xiphoid process	ventral border of the humerus	adduction of the humerus
peroneus brevis	distal one-half of the fibula	the first phalanx of the fifth digit	flexion of the pes
peroneus longus	lateral surface of the fibula	proximal ends of all five metatarsals	flexion of the pes
peroneus tertius	lateral surface of the fibula	the first phalanx of the fifth digit	flexes the pes and abducts and extends the fifth digit
piriformis	transverse processes of the last two sacral and first caudal vertebrae	greater trochanter of the femur	abducts the thigh
plantaris	sesamoid bone near the lateral epicondyle of the femur	calcaneus	extends the pes
popliteus	lateral epicondyle of the femur	proximal end of the tibia	flexes and medially rotates the shank
pronator quadratus	shaft of ulna	shaft of radius	pronates of the manus by rotating the radius
pronator teres	medial epicondyle of the humerus	medial border of the radius	pronates the manus by rotating the radius
psoas major	lesser trochanter of the femur	last thoracic and each of the lumbar vertebrae	flex and rotate the thigh
psoas minor	last thoracic and first three lumbar vertebrae	pubis	flexes the pelvis toward the abdomen

quadratus femoris	ischial tuberosity	ventral borders of the greater and lesser trochanters	laterally rotates the thigh
rectus abdominis	iliac crest	cartilage of the fifth through seventh ribs and the xiphoid	flexes the vertebral column and compresses the abdomen
rhomboideus capitis	lambdoidal ridge	cranial end of the vertebral border of the scapula	cranial rotation of the scapula
rhomboideus cervicis	first four thoracic vertebrae	middle vertebral border of the scapula	adducts the scapula
rhomboideus thoracis	first four thoracic vertebrae	caudal end of the scapula's vertebral border	adducts the scapula
rectus femoris	ilium near the acetabulum	tibial tuberosity	extend the shank at the knee joint
sartorius	iliac crest	fascia surrounding the knee and tibia	adduction and rotation of the femur, and extension of the shank
scalenus	various locations on the ribs	transverse processes of the cervical vertebrae	pull the ribs cranially to expand the thorax
semimembranosus	tuberosity and ramus of the ischium	medial epicondyle at the distal end of the femur	extends the thigh
semispinalis capitis	cervical vertebrae 3-7	first 3 thoracic vertebrae	elevation of the head
semispinalis cervicis	seventh cervical and first three thoracic vertebrae	lambdoidal crest of the occipital bone	elevation of the head
semitendinosus	ischial tuberosity	medial surface of the tibia	flexes the shank
serratus dorsalis caudalis	middorsal fascia	last four or five ribs	draws the ribs in a caudal direction
serratus dorsalis cranialis	middorsal fascia	first nine ribs	draws the ribs in a cranial direction
serratus ventralis	first nine or ten ribs and last five cervical vertebrae	vertebral border of the scapula	draws the scapula toward the thoracic wall
soleus	proximal one-third of the fibula	calcaneus	extends the pes
spinodeltoid	spine of the scapula	greater tuberosity of the humerus	protracts the humerus
spinotrapezius	spinous processes of the thoracic vertebrae	fascia of the supraspinatus and infraspinatus muscles	pulls the scapula caudally
splenius	fascia along the middorsal line of the neck	lambdoidal ridge of the occipital bone	lateral flexion of the head
spinalis dorsi	neural spines of the more caudal thoracic vertebra	transverse processes of the more cranial vertebrae	extension of the vertebral column
sternohyoid	first costal cartilage	hyoid bone	retracts the hyoid bone

sternomastoid	cranial border of the manubrium	lambdoidal ridge and mastoid process of the temporal bone	when the sternomastoids from each side contract simultaneously, they flex the head; individual contraction rotates the head
sternothyroid	first costal cartilage	thyroid cartilage of the larynx	retracts the hyoid bone
styloglossus	the mastoid process of the temporal bone	base of the tongue	retracts and elevates the tongue
stylohyoid	hyoid bone	hyoid bone	elevation of the hyoid bone
subscapularis	subscapular fossa of the scapula	dorsal border of the lesser tuberosity of the humerus	adducts the humerus
supinator	lateral epicondyle of the humerus	proximal one-third of the radius	supinates the antebrachium
supraspinatus	supraspinous fossa of the scapula	greater tuberosity of the humerus	protracts the humerus
temporalis	temporal bone	coronoid process of the mandible	elevates the mandible
tensor fascia latae	ventral border of the ilium and fascia of nearby hip muscles	fascia lata to the surface of the patella	extend the shank
tenuissimus	second caudal vertebra	ischial tuberosity	abducts the thigh and flexes the shank
teres major	the axillary border of the scapula	proximal end of the humerus	medially flexes and rotates the humerus
teres minor	scapula near the glenoid fossa	the greater tuberosity of the humerus	laterally rotates the humerus
thyrohyoid	thyroid cartilage of the larynx on the lateral side	hyoid bone	protracts the larynx
tibialis cranialis	the proximal end of the tibia and fibula	first metatarsal	flexion of the pes
transverse abdominis	aponeurosis of the caudal costal cartilages, lumbar vertebrae, and ventral border of the ilium	linea alba	compresses the abdomen
transverse costarum	sternum	first rib and costal cartilage	pulls the ribs cranially
transverse thoracis	dorsolateral border of the sternum from the third to the eighth rib	costal cartilages	draws the ribs downward
triceps brachii	three heads of origin: a lateral head from the deltoid ridge of the humerus; a long head from the axillary border of the scapula near the glenoid fossa; and a medial head from the medial side of the humerus	olecranon of the ulna	extension of the antebrachium
xiphihumeralis	xiphoid process	ventral border of the humerus	adduction of the humerus

CHAPTER REVIEW

A. Answer the following multiple-choice questions by circling the most correct answer.

1. The connective tissue associated with a muscle is known as
   a. fascia
   b. areolar tissue
   c. fat
   d. ligament

2. A tendon that attaches a muscle to a moveable bone is known as a
   a. tendon of origin
   b. tendon of insertion
   c. aponeurosis
   d. ligament

3. A muscle action in which the angle between opposing bones is decreased is known as:
   a. circumduction
   b. flexion
   c. extension
   d. adduction

4. To view a deep muscle, the superficial muscle must be _____ and reflected first.
   a. removed
   b. transected
   c. pushed aside
   d. cleaned

5. The largest muscle of the pectoral region is the
   a. xiphihumeralis
   b. pectoralis minor
   c. pectoralis major
   d. external oblique

6. The deepest of the large abdominal muscles is the
   a. external oblique
   b. internal oblique
   c. transverse abdominis
   d. rectus abdominis

7. Which muscle includes three heads of origin, and is the primary extensor of the brachium?
   a. biceps brachii
   b. triceps brachii
   c. quadriceps femoris
   d. epitrochlearis

8. The rectus femoris and vastus lateralis form part of which muscle group?
   a. quadriceps femoris
   b. iliopsoas
   c. forearm flexors
   d. superficial neck muscles

9. Which of the following muscle groups abducts the thigh?
   a. quadriceps femoris
   b. gluteus muscles
   c. gastrocnemius
   d. hamstring muscles

10. Which of the following muscles flexes the pes?
    a. flexor digitorum longus
    b. tibialis cranialis
    c. extensor carpi ulnaris
    d. flexor carpi radialis

B. Complete the sentences below by providing the missing terms from the chapter material.

1. A broad, thin sheet of fascia that functions as a tendon is called an _____.

2. Muscles can be separated with a blunt probe because they are individually wrapped with a layer of _____.

3. Movement of a limb toward the body's midline is called _____.

4. The most superficial muscle of the pectoral region, which is not found in humans, is called the _____.

5. The clavotrapezius, acromiotrapezius, and spinotrapezius muscles of the cat are represented by a single muscle in the human called the _____.

6. A small muscle on the craniolateral surface of the humerus, which functions as a synergist with the biceps brachii to flex the antebrachium, is called the _____.

7. The _____ supinates the manus, and is the long, slender muscle on the cranial surface of the forearm.

8. The tensor fascia lata inserts on a large aponeurosis that wraps round the knee, called the _____ _____.

9. The large muscle dominating the lateral surface of the cat's thigh is the _____ _____, which abducts the thigh and flexes the shank.

10. The _____ _____ is a large fan-shaped muscle of the lateral thorax. It draws the scapula toward the thoracic wall.

C. Answer the following descriptive and critical thinking questions with a brief explanation in the spaces provided.

1. Explain the role and relative importance of the quadriceps femoris group. Include a comparison between quadripeds and bipeds in your answer.

_____

_____

_____

_____

_____

2. Compare and contrast the gluteus muscles in the cat and human. _____

    _____

    _____

    _____

    _____

    _____

    _____

3. How does the biceps brachii differ between cats and humans? _____

    _____

    _____

    _____

    _____

    _____

c h a p t e r   f o u r

THE DIGESTIVE SYSTEM

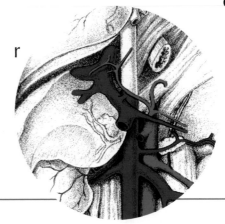

The digestive system is structurally divided into two main parts: a long, winding tube that carries food through its length, and a series of supportive organs outside of the tube. The long tube is called the **gastrointestinal (GI) tract**. The GI tract extends from the mouth to the anus, and consists of the mouth, or oral cavity, the pharynx, the esophagus, the stomach, the small intestine, and the large intestine. It is here that the functions of mechanical digestion, chemical digestion, absorption of nutrients and water, and release of solid waste material take place. The supportive organs that lie outside the GI tract are known as **accessory organs**, and include the teeth, salivary glands, liver, gallbladder, and pancreas.

Because most organs of the digestive system lie within body cavities, you will perform a dissection procedure that exposes the cavities before you begin identifying individual organs. You will also observe the cavities and their associated membranes before proceeding with your study of the digestive system.

EXPOSING THE BODY CAVITIES

With your skinned cat on its dorsal side, examine the cutting lines shown in Figure 4.1 and plan out your dissection. Note that the numbers indicate the sequence of the cutting procedure. Palpate the long, bony sternum and the softer, cartilaginous xiphoid process to find the ventral midline. Then, follow these instructions:

1. Begin your #1 incision by inserting the point of your scissors through the muscle layers about ¼-inch caudal to the tip of the xiphoid process. Make the cut large enough for your finger to poke through, then insert your finger into the body cavity to feel the space beneath the muscle layers. Your incision was very likely made just caudal to the **diaphragm**, an internal muscular partition dividing the thoracic and abdominopelvic cavities. Press your finger gently against the diaphragm; it

should feel like the wall of a stretched balloon.

2. Extend the cut laterally in both directions, roughly 4 inches, still working with your scissors. Cut in a curved pattern as shown in Figure 4.1, which follows the contour of the diaphragm. Make your cut through all muscle layers and connective tissue, but be careful to avoid cutting too deeply and damaging the underlying organs. Find the diaphragm again, and with a scalpel, carefully cut it from its attachments to the ventral body wall. Allow the diaphragm to remain on top of the liver.

3. From your first incision, use your scissors to cut in a longitudinal direction roughly ¼-inch to one side of the ventral midline. While cutting, pull upward (toward you) with the scissors to create a space

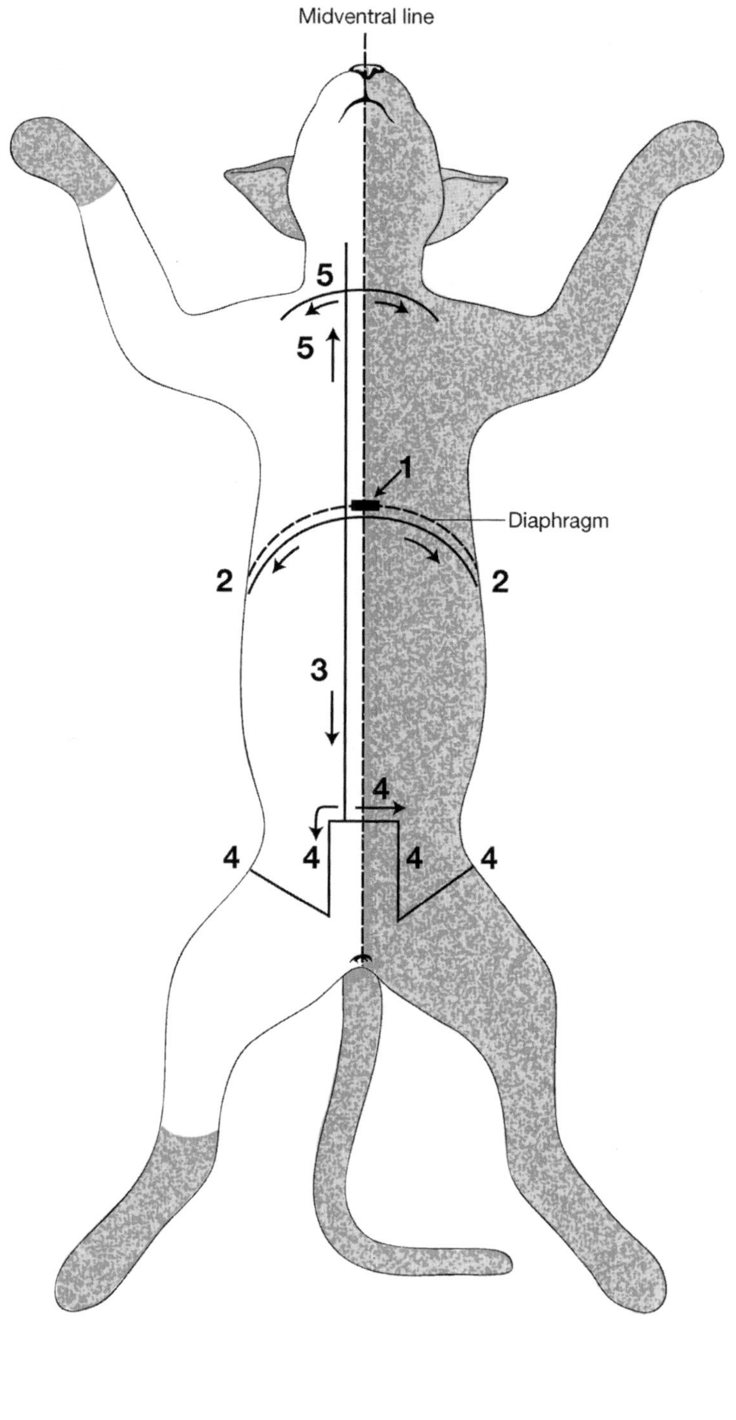

Figure 4.1 – Cutting guide for exposing
body cavities (the numbers correspond to the sequences in the text).

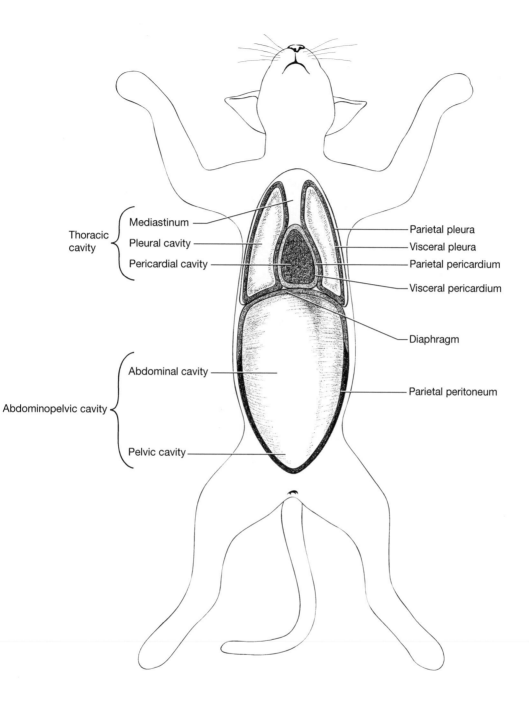

Figure 4.2 – Ventral body cavities.

between the body wall and the visceral organs. If performed carefully, this technique will help prevent the scissors from cutting into the organs.

4. Extend your cut down one side of the ventral midline caudally at first, but stop when you feel the resistance of a membrane near the urinary bladder. Then cut laterally about ½ inch, then caudally another ½ inch, then continue the horizontal cut to the iliac crest (see Figure 4.1). These cuts will enable you to cut around the genital region without damaging it.

5. Now you are ready to expose the thoracic cavity. Extend your midventral incision toward the neck region from the #1 incision near the xiphoid process, and cut in a cranial direction. As you reach the neck region, you will have to proceed very slowly to avoid damaging the arteries (colored red with latex), veins (colored blue with latex), and nerves (white). Cut only muscle tissue to expose the organs lying deep in the neck, including the trachea, thyroid gland, and larynx.

6. With your cutting complete, reflect the thoracic and abdominal walls to reveal the internal cavities. You will have to fracture ribs to reflect the thoracic wall, so press the walls laterally until you hear the snapping sound. Since the fractured ends of the ribs can be sharp, take care to avoid cutting yourself.

VENTRAL BODY CAVITIES AND MEMBRANES

Now that you've exposed the ventral body cavities and their associated membranes, identify them from the descriptions that follow (Figure 4.2). The ventral body cavity is also known as the **coelom**, or **coelomic cavity**.

Thoracic Cavity

The thoracic cavity is the potential space located cranial to the diaphragm. It is lined by a moist membrane called the **parietal pleura**. The parietal pleura continues inward to cover both lungs, forming the **visceral pleura**. Between the two pleural membranes is a moist space called the **pleural cavity**. The thoracic cavity also includes the **pericardial cavity** along its midline, which contains the heart. The pericardial cavity is sandwiched between two layers of the **pericardium**, which includes an outer **parietal pericardium** (or pericardial sac) and an inner **visceral pericardium**. In addition, the potential space located cranial to the heart is known as the **mediastinum**, which contains the major vessels of the heart and the thymus gland.

Abdominopelvic Cavity

The abdominopelvic cavity is the large cavity located caudal to the diaphragm. It is lined by a membrane attached to the inner body wall called the **parietal peritoneum**. The parietal peritoneum extends inward to wrap around many of the organs of the abdominoplevic cavity. The part of the peritoneum covering most of the visceral organs is known as the **visceral peritoneum**. The cavity between the two peritoneal membranes is called the **peritoneal cavity**, and contains a small amount of fluid that helps reduce friction between adjacent visceral organs. The peritoneum also includes numerous extensions, or folds, which will be described later in this chapter. The abdominopelvic cavity contains many visceral organs, including the stomach, small intestine, large intestine, liver, pancreas, gallbladder, internal reproductive organs, and more. Its larger cranial portion is the **abdominal cavity**, which extends from the diaphragm to the level of the iliac crest. The smaller caudal area is the bowl-shaped **pelvic cavity**.

CRANIAL DIGESTIVE STRUCTURES

The organs and associated structures of the digestive system will be described sequentially from the

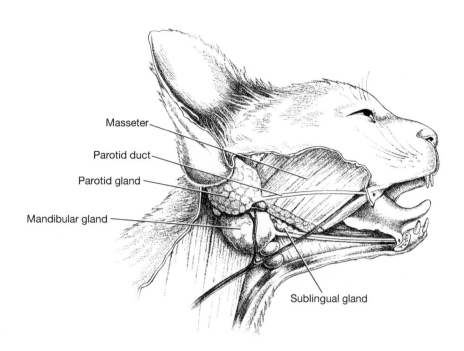

Masseter

Parotid duct

Parotid gland

Mandibular gland

Sublingual gland

© bluedoor, LLC

Figure 4.3 – Salivary glands (lateral view of the head and neck).

salivary glands around the mouth to the anus. The system has been divided into a cranial portion and a caudal portion, with the diaphragm serving as the line of division between the two. The cranial digestive structures include the salivary glands, oral cavity, pharynx, and esophagus. Locate each structure in your cat and identify its characteristic features.

Salivary Glands

To expose the **salivary glands**, carefully remove any connective tissue and fat that remains on the lateral side of the head and neck, especially on the surface of the masseter muscle. Be very careful to avoid damaging blood vessels, nerves, and small tubes that you see as you clean.

The salivary glands are located in the head region surrounding the oral cavity. They are soft, lobular structures that connect to the oral cavity by way of a duct. Salivary glands are exocrine glands that secrete a watery fluid, saliva, into ducts that carry it into the oral cavity when food is present. The cat has three major salivary glands and two minor glands.

PAROTID GLANDS: the largest of the salivary glands, they are paired structures located superficial to the masseter muscle on each side of the head just below the ear (Figure 4.3). Emerging from its rostral surface is the **parotid duct**, which crosses over the masseter muscle before entering the vestibule (space between the teeth and the lip). It opens opposite to the third upper premolar tooth.

MANDIBULAR GLANDS: paired glands, each located immediately ventral to the parotid gland and posterior to the angle of the mandible (Figure 4.3). The duct emerges from the anterior edge of each gland, then extends laterally beneath the digastric muscle to enter the floor of the oral cavity just anterior to the lingual frenulum (beneath the tongue).

SUBLINGUAL GLANDS: small, paired glands located at the anterior end of each mandibular gland. The sublingual duct extends parallel to the submandibular duct, although it is smaller and difficult to observe.

MOLAR GLANDS: a minor pair of salivary glands in the cat, each located at the angle of the jaw immediately deep to the skin (not shown). Several small, inconspicuous ducts open at the inner surface of the cheeks.

ZYGOMATIC GLANDS: a minor pair of salivary glands, each located in the floor of the eye orbit (not shown). A small duct from each gland opens at the posterolateral part of the roof of the mouth.

The salivary glands of humans include the large parotid glands, the submandibular glands, and the sublingual glands. The parotids are located similarly to those of the cat, and the parotid duct opens into the vestibule opposite the second maxillary molar tooth. The submandibulars are paralleled by the mandibulars in the cat. The sublinguals are located anterior to the submandibulars at the base of the tongue, and the sublingual duct opens into the floor of the oral cavity directly above the glands. Humans do not have molar and zygomatic glands.

Oral Cavity

To expose the mouth, or **oral cavity**, cut through the muscles and connective tissue suspending the jaw on one side of your cat. Using bone shears, cut the condyloid portion of the mandible on the same side. Pry the mouth open, and locate the following structures of the oral cavity (Figure 4.4).

VESTIBULE: the part of the oral cavity located between the teeth and cheeks. Notice the **labial frenulum**, which is a fold of tissue through the midline of the vestibule connecting the upper and lower lips.

TEETH: the dental formula for the cat is as follows: for the upper jaw, 6 incisors, 2 canines, 3 premolars, and 2 molars (6:2:3:2); for the lower jaw, 6 incisors, 2 canines, 4 premolars, and 2 molars (6:2:4:2). This dentition reflects adaptations for a carnivorous diet. *The comparative dental formula for adult humans is the same for both jaws: 4 incisors, 2 canines, 4 premolars, and 6 molars. Also, the human canines are shorter and more blunt, and the molars are more flat, which reflect the omnivore diet that includes less cutting and ripping, and more grinding.*

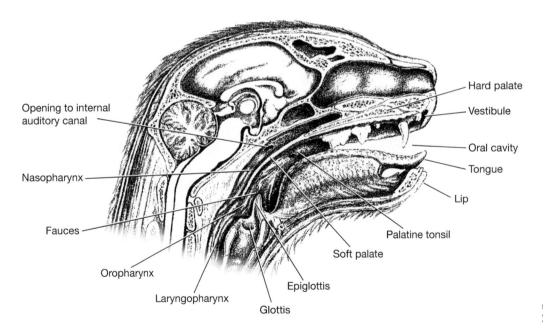

© bluedoor, LLC

Figure 4.4 – Oral cavity and pharynx.

HARD PALATE: the rostral portion of the roof of the oral cavity. It is formed by the maxillary and palatine bones and is lined with mucous membrane.

SOFT PALATE: caudal to the hard palate, it is a muscular partition between the oral cavity and nasal cavity, and is lined with mucous membrane.

TONGUE: the large, muscular organ that makes up the floor of the oral cavity. It is attached to the floor of the mouth by a ventral fold of tissue called the **lingual frenulum**. The frenulum can be seen when the tongue is lifted from the floor. The tongue's surface contains four types of elevated structures called **papillae**, which house the taste buds for the reception of taste. In the cat, the most common papillae are the **filiform**, which include sharp projections to give the cat a friction surface for grooming. Other papillae include the mushroom-shaped **fungiform**, the large, rounded **vallate**, and the leaf-shaped **foliate**. *The human tongue is very similar, except filiform papillae are less abundant and not as sharply pointed, and foliate papillae are not present.*

PALATOGLOSSAL ARCHES: lateral folds on both sides of the oral cavity wall, extending from the caudal portion of the tongue to the soft palate. They represent the boundary between the oral cavity and the pharynx.

FAUCES: the opening at the extreme caudal portion of the oral cavity between the palatoglossal arches. The fauces leads into the oropharynx.

Pharynx

The **pharynx** is the chamber located caudal to the fauces, extending from the oral cavity to the larynx (Figure 4.4). It provides a passageway for air traveling to and from the lungs and for food traveling from the mouth to the esophagus. It is commonly divided into three sections, the nasopharynx, oropharynx, and laryngopharynx.

NASOPHARYNX: the cranial part of the pharynx. To view it, make a longitudinal incision along the midline of the soft palate, and carefully pry the two sections apart as far as possible. If one is available, shine a light into the cavity. In the lateral walls of the nasopharynx are the openings to the paired **internal auditory canals**, which communicate with the middle ear.

OROPHARYNX: located between the palatoglossal arches and the free caudal margin of the soft palate. The oropharynx communicates with the oral cavity through the fauces. Embedded within its laterodorsal walls are a pair of **palatine tonsils**, each of which lies partially recessed in a shallow depression called the tonsilar fossae.

LARYNGOPHARYNX: the caudal part of the pharynx. It extends from the oropharynx to the larynx. Its slit-like opening to the larynx is called the **glottis**, which is protected from passing food particles by a movable fold known as the **epiglottis**.

Esophagus

The **esophagus** is long, muscular tube that transports swallowed material from the pharynx to the stomach. It lies dorsal to the trachea and travels the length of the thoracic cavity. At its caudal end it penetrates the diaphragm to unite with the stomach in the abdominal cavity. Because it is located in the thoracic cavity dorsal to the heart and lungs, the esophagus will not be dissected at this time, but you will be able to observe it during your study of the respiratory system (Chapter 5).

CAUDAL DIGESTIVE STRUCTURES

The structures of the digestion system located caudal to the diaphragm include the liver, gallbladder, stomach, pancreas, small intestine, and large intestine. To observe these organs and their associated structures, pull back the flaps of the abdominal wall to expose the abdominopelvic cavity.

Peritoneum

The **peritoneum** is the extensive serous membrane of the abdominopelvic cavity, which you observed when you initially opened the cavity.

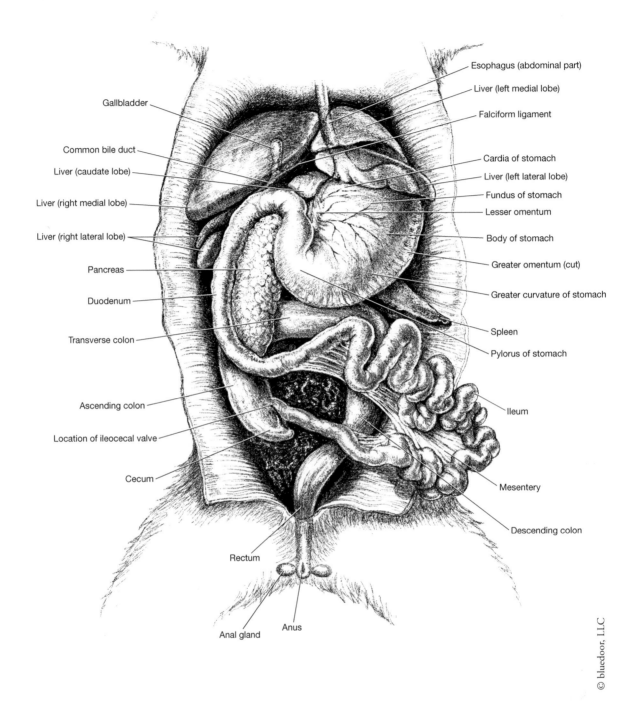

Gallbladder

Common bile duct

Liver (caudate lobe)

Liver (right medial lobe)

Liver (right lateral lobe)

Pancreas

Duodenum

Transverse colon

Ascending colon

Location of ileocecal valve

Cecum

Rectum

Anal gland

Anus

Esophagus (abdominal part)

Liver (left medial lobe)

Falciform ligament

Cardia of stomach

Liver (left lateral lobe)

Fundus of stomach

Lesser omentum

Body of stomach

Greater omentum (cut)

Greater curvature of stomach

Spleen

Pylorus of stomach

Ileum

Mesentery

Descending colon

© bluedoor, LLC

Figure 4.5 – Organs and peritoneum of the abdominopelvic cavity.

The **peritoneal folds** are extensions of the visceral and parietal peritonea, and include the following (Figure 4.5):

FALCIFORM LIGAMENT: a double-layered extension of the visceral peritoneum of the liver. It anchors the liver to the dorsal wall of the abdomen and the diaphragm, and separates the liver into right and left lobes.

MESENTERY: a double layer of peritoneum that extends from the visceral peritoneum of the small and large intestines to the dorsal abdominal wall. The portion that suspends the small intestine is called the **mesentery proper**, the part supporting the large intestine

is the **mesocolon**, and the part attached to the rectum is the **mesorectum**. Note that the pancreas is located within the mesentery proper.

LESSER OMENTUM: a double layer of peritoneum extending from the lesser curvature of the stomach and the duodenum of the small intestine to the liver. Notice the common bile duct, which is located on the free edge of the lesser omentum. This duct transports bile from the liver and gallbladder to the duodenum.

GREATER OMENTUM: a double layer of peritoneum that extends from the greater curvature of the stomach to the dorsal abdomi-

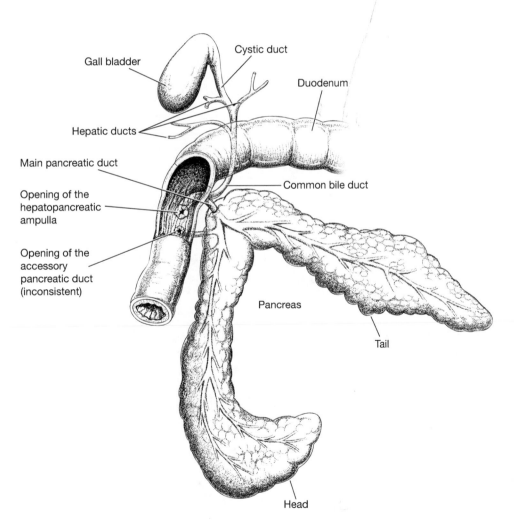

Figure 4.6 – Gallbladder, biliary ducts, and pancreas.

nal wall. The double-layered sac extending ventrocaudally to the small intestine is called the **omental bursa**, or lesser peritoneal sac, and contains fat deposits, lymph nodes, and lymphatic vessels.

Liver

The **liver** is the prominent, dark-brown organ lying immediately deep to the diaphragm, with most of its bulk on the right side (Figure 4.5). Its functions include management of sugar and fat levels in the blood, storage of toxins, and production of a yellow-green fluid that breaks down fats, called bile. In the cat, the liver is divided into six lobes. Identify the falciform ligament once again, which divides the liver into right and left portions. The left side of the liver includes a **left medial lobe** and a **left lateral lobe**. The right side of the liver includes a **quadrate lobe** adjacent to the falciform ligament, which is partially united with the **right medial lobe**. Between these two lobes is a depression that contains the greenish sac known as the gallbladder. Dorsolateral to the right medial lobe is the **right lateral lobe**, and dorsal to it is the smaller **caudate lobe**. *The human liver is also a prominent organ, but contains only four lobes: a large right lobe separated from the smaller left lobe by the falciform ligament, a quadrate lobe, and a caudate lobe.*

Gallbladder

Elevate the right medial lobe and quadrate lobe of the liver to observe the **gallbladder**, located in a depression between the two lobes, known as the cystic fossa (Figures 4.5 and 4.6). The gallbladder is a thin-walled sac that receives newly manufactured bile from the liver for temporary storage. When a meal is consumed, the gallbladder contracts to push bile into the **cystic duct**. The cystic duct combines with numerous **hepatic ducts** arising from the left lobes and right lateral lobe of the liver to form the **common bile duct**. The common bile duct extends caudally to unite with the duodenum of the small intestine at the hepatopancreatic ampulla. Once in the small intestine, bile assists in the digestion of fats.

Stomach

The stomach is a J-shaped enlargement of the GI tract, located directly beneath the diaphragm on the left side of the abdominal cavity (Figure 4.5). It functions as a temporary reservoir for swallowed food, and its inner lining contains **gastric glands** that secrete hydrochloric acid and the enzyme pepsinogen to begin the process of protein digestion. The lateral border of the stomach forms a rounded, convex surface called the **greater curvature,** and its medial border forms a concave angle known as the **lesser curvature.** Note the peritoneal fold called the greater omentum, which originates from the greater curvature to hang downward. Also note the flat, elongate, dark-reddish **spleen** near the left dorsolateral surface of the greater curvature. The spleen is part of the lymphatic system. Similar to the human stomach, the stomach of the cat is divided into the following parts:

CARDIA: the part of the stomach that receives the esophagus. It surrounds the **lower esophageal sphincter**, the ring of muscle that separates the stomach from the esophagus.

FUNDUS: a sac-like, rounded portion that extends laterally to the cardia and slightly craniad.

BODY: the large, central portion of the stomach, which is located caudal to the fundus.

PYLORUS: the narrow, caudal part that communicates with the duodenum of the small intestine via a sphincter muscle called the **pyloric valve.**

Once you've identified the parts of the stomach, make an incision along the greater curvature from the fundus to the pylorus, taking great care to avoid damaging the greater omentum. Notice the folds in the wall of the stomach, which are called **rugae.** They allow the organ to expand with incoming food.

Small Intestine

The small intestine is a long, winding tube that extends from the pyloric valve of the stomach to its junction with the large intestine (Figure 4.5). The small intestine finalizes chemical digestion and is the only site for nutrient absorption. Its inner lining is characterized by the presence of tiny, fingerlike **villi**, which increase its absorptive surface area. Similar to the human small intestine, the small intestine of the cat is divided into three segments:

DUODENUM: the largest of the three segments in diameter, but the shortest in length, it extends from the pyloric valve to its union with the jejunum. In the cat, it ranges in length from 12-18 cm (5-7 inches). The duodenum receives the common bile duct from the liver and gallbladder and the pancreatic duct from the pancreas.

JEJUNUM: the middle segment of the small intestine, it is the longest, with an average length of about 50 cm (20 inches) in the cat.

ILEUM: the caudal segment, it extends from its union with the jejunum to the large intestine about 35 cm (14 inches) in the cat. A doughnut-shaped muscle called the **ileocecal valve** surrounds the junction of the ileum and large intestine. Similar to the pyloric valve, it regulates the movement of materials from one organ (the small intestine) to the next (the large intestine), and prevents the reflux of contents in the opposite direction.

Large Intestine

The caudal portion of the GI tract, the large intestine extends from the ileocecal valve to the anus (Figure 4.5). It gets its name from being larger in diameter along its entire length than the small intestine, although it is roughly one-third the length. The large intestine absorbs water from the contents that arrive from the small intestine, and prepares and forms the feces. Smooth muscles in the wall of the large intestine contract to move the feces and release it during defecation. The large intestine contains the following segments:

CECUM: the cranial segment, which communicates with the ileum via the ileocecal valve. It is a short, blind diverticulum in the right caudal aspect of the abdominal cavity. *The human cecum includes a fingerlike tube extend-*

ing from it, known as the appendix, which is lacking in the cat.

COLON: a long, wide segment extending from the cecum to the rectum. The colon is divided into an **ascending colon**, which ascends from its union with the cecum to the area occupied by the liver; a **transverse colon** that travels transversely from the right side near the liver to the left side of the cranial abdominal cavity; and a **descending colon**, which curves caudally to descend to the pelvic cavity.

RECTUM: the terminal segment of the large intestine. The short rectum opens to the exterior via the **anus**, which is surrounded by sphincter muscles. A pair of scent glands, known as **anal glands**, open into the rectum near the anus. Secretions from the anal glands are important for marking territorial boundaries. *The large intestine of the human is similar to that of the cat, except the human includes a sigmoid colon between the descending colon and rectum, which is an S-shaped curvature. Also, humans lack anal glands.*

Pancreas

The **pancreas** is a diffuse mass of soft glandular tissue located within the mesentery proper of the small intestine (Figures 4.5 and 4.6). It is located just below the greater curvature of the stomach, and slightly dorsal to it, and includes a caudal head portion and a cranial tail portion. The pancreas functions in the secretion of hormones that regulate blood sugar levels, and also in the secretion of digestive enzymes and sodium bicarbonate. The digestive enzymes and sodium bicarbonate form the pancreatic juice, which is channeled out of the pancreas by the main **pancreatic duct**. This duct unites with the common bile duct to be delivered into the duodenum. At the union of the common bile duct and duodenum is a small elevation known as the ampulla of Vater, or **hepatopancreatic ampulla**. An accessory duct may also be present.

CHAPTER REVIEW

A. Answer the following multiple-choice questions by circling the most correct answer.

1. Which of the following organs forms part of the GI tract?
   a. stomach
   b. peritoneum
   c. tongue
   d. liver

2. The digestive organ that is the site of nutrient absorption is the
   a. liver
   b. stomach
   c. small intestine
   d. esophagus

3. The membrane that lines the thoracic wall is the
   a. pericardium
   b. parietal peritoneum
   c. parietal pleura
   d. greater omentum

4. The structure that separates the thoracic and abdominoplevic cavities is called the
   a. diaphragm
   b. pericardial sac
   c. falciform ligament
   d. lesser omentum

5. The abdominopelvic cavity contains
   a. the abdominal cavity
   b. the stomach
   c. the large intestine
   d. all of the above

6. The largest of the salivary glands are
   a. the maxillary glands
   b. located on the tongue
   c. the parotid glands
   d. do not produce saliva

7. The prominent, brown organ beneath the diaphragm on the right side is the
   a. pancreas
   b. liver
   c. duodenum
   d. gallbladder

8. The soft, glandular organ that provides digestive enzymes to the duodenum is the
   a. liver
   b. pancreas
   c. stomach
   d. gallbladder

9. The segments of the large intestine are the
   a. cecum, colon, and rectum
   b. duodenum, jejunum, and ileum
   c. cardia, body, and pylorus
   d. none of the above

10. The first abdominopelvic structure receiving food is the
    a. duodenum
    b. stomach
    c. cecum
    d. pharynx

B. Complete the sentences below by providing the missing terms from the chapter material.

1. The liver, pancreas, and salivary glands are _____ _____ of the digestive system.

2. The membrane attached to the inner wall of the abdominopelvic cavity is the _____ _____.

3. The larger, cranial portion of the abdominopelvic cavity is known as the _____ _____.

4. The paired glands located immediately ventral to the parotid gland and posterior to the angle of the mandible are the _____ _____.

5. The rostral portion of the roof of the oral cavity is called the _____ _____.

6. The _____ is attached to the floor of the mouth by a ventral fold of tissue called the lingual frenulum.

7. The part of the cat's throat that contains the palatine tonsils is the _____.

8. A double layer of peritoneum that extends from the visceral peritoneum of the small and large intestines to the dorsal abdominal wall is known as the _____.

9. Bile is channeled into the duodenum from the _____ by way of the common bile duct.

10. The union of the small and large intestines is marked by a valve called the _____ valve.

C. Answer the following descriptive and critical-thinking questions with a brief explanation in the spaces provided.

1. Describe the process of digestion by including contributions by the oral cavity, salivary glands, stomach, and small intestine.

   _____

   _____

   _____

   _____

   _____

2. Describe the contributions to the function of digestion by the liver, gallbladder, and pancreas.

_____

_____

_____

_____

_____

_____

3. Based on the anatomical similarities between cats and humans, suggest the type of diet that humans are adapted for and explain why.

_____

_____

_____

_____

_____

_____

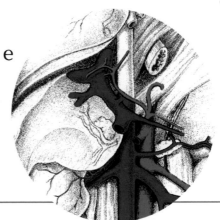

chapter five

THE RESPIRATORY SYSTEM

The **respiratory system** brings oxygen into the bloodstream, which transports it to all body cells. It also removes the waste product carbon dioxide from the blood and channels it outside the body. The process of oxygen delivery and carbon dioxide removal from the blood is called **gas exchange**. It is a vital function, due to the oxygen demand by cells for supporting metabolism and the toxic results of a buildup of carbon dioxide.

The first step in bringing oxygen into the blood occurs during inhalation, or **inspiration**, which is initiated by expansion of the thoracic cavity as a result of respiratory muscle contraction. The most important respiratory muscle is the **diaphragm**, which separates the thoracic and abdominopelvic cavities in mammals. During inspiration, air moves from the outside environment to the air sacs within the lungs, which are known as alveoli. Exhaling air results when the respiratory muscles relax, and is called **expiration**. Together, inspiration and expiration are known as **ventilation**.

The second step of respiration begins when fresh air has filled the lungs. The air molecules diffuse between the alveoli and the surrounding capillaries. Due to pressure differences, oxygen moves out of the alveoli and into the capillaries, and carbon dioxide moves in the opposite direction. This process is known as **external respiration**.

The third step of respiration is called **internal respiration**. It occurs when oxygen carried in the bloodstream diffuses into surrounding body cells, and carbon dioxide moves from the cells into the bloodstream.

The final step of respiration occurs when the body exhales, or expires, pushing air containing carbon dioxide out of the lungs and body.

The respiratory system consists of organs that support the activities of ventilation and external respiration. It includes a series of chambers and tubes that carry air to and from the lungs and the alveoli within the lungs where external respiration takes place.

In this chapter you will study the organs and associated structures of the respiratory system. For convenience of discussion, they have been divided into cranial respiratory structures, which are located cranial to the thoracic cavity, and caudal respiratory structures, which lie within the thoracic cavity.

CRANIAL RESPIRATORY STRUCTURES

The respiratory organs that are located cranial to the thoracic cavity include the nose, pharynx, larynx, and trachea. With your cat on its dorsal side, identify the following cranial structures:

Nose

The nose, or **rostrum**, is the initial warming chamber for incoming air (Figure 5.1). Its internal chamber, the **nasal cavity**, lies between the nostrils, called the **external nares**, and the openings to the throat called the **internal nares**, or **choanae**. Also, it is located cranial to the palate. The nasal cavity is divided by a vertical partition

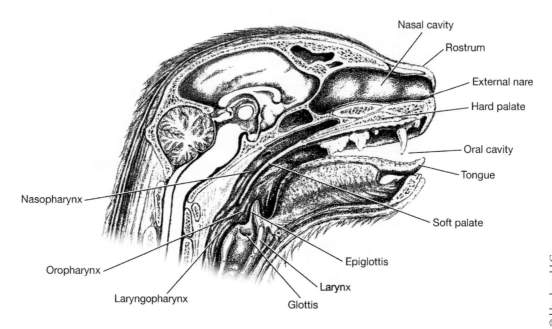

Figure 5.1 – Nose and pharynx (midsagittal section of head).

dividing the nasal cavity into right and left **nasal chambers**, or **nasal fossae**. The partition is composed of the vomer, the perpendicular plate of the ethmoid bone, and cartilage. The nasal fossae include channels that warm and moisten inspired air as it passes through, called **nasal meati**. The two meati within each nasal fossa are formed by the turbinate bones.

Pharynx

You observed the pharynx during your dissection of the digestive system. Recall that it includes three sections, the **nasopharynx, oropharynx**, and **laryngopharynx** (Figure 5.1). The nasopharynx receives air that exits the choanae. From this upper chamber, air moves into the oropharynx, then the laryngopharynx. From here, air moves into the larynx.

Larynx

The larynx is a box-like structure composed of five cartilages that create a small chamber between the laryngopharynx and the trachea (Figures 5.1 and 5.2). The larynx houses the vocal cords, which produce sound when exhaled air is channeled through. To observe the larynx in your specimen, clear away any remaining tissue in the upper throat area. Notice the thyroid cartilage and identify the following parts:

GLOTTIS: the opening between the laryngopharynx and the larynx.

EPIGLOTTIS: a thin, leaf-shaped single cartilage located cranial to the glottis. During swallowing, it covers the glottis as pharyngeal muscles elevate the larynx to contact it, creating a lid that prevents the passage of food and water into the larynx. The epiglottis is attached to the large thyroid cartilage at its base.

THYROID CARTILAGE: the most prominent of the laryngeal cartilages, it is a single cartilage that forms most of the ventral wall of the larynx. It is larger in males than in females, and *in human males it is commonly referred to as the "adam's apple"*.

CRICOID CARTILAGE: located caudal to the thyroid cartilage, it is an unpaired ring-like cartilage that forms the caudal walls of the larynx. It is attached to the first ring of tracheal cartilage.

ARYTENOID CARTILAGES: located dorsal to the thyroid cartilage at the margin of the glottis, these small, paired cartilages serve as the point of origin of the vocal cords.

VOCAL CORDS: to observe these, carefully cut open the larynx along the midventral line. The pair of whitish, lateral folds that extend from the arytenoids to the thyroid cartilage

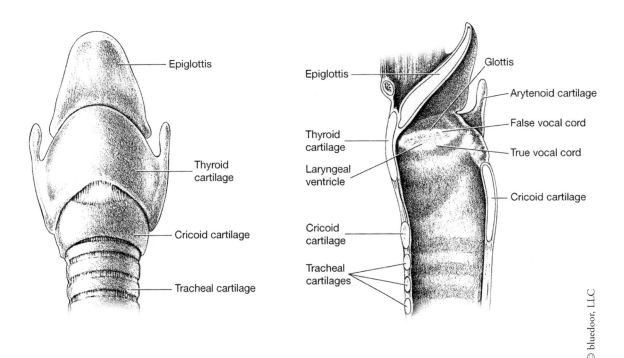

Figure 5.2 – Larynx (ventral and sectioned lateral views).

on the dorsal side are known as the **true vocal cords**, and the pair of lateral folds on the ventral side are known as **false vocal cords**. Sound production in cats is the result of exhaled air movement across the true vocal cords, while purring is likely caused by the vibration of the glottis.

The human larynx also includes the cuneiform and corniculate cartilages in the posterior side of the larynx.

Trachea

The trachea is a tubular air passageway extending from the larynx to the level of the 5th thoracic vertebra, where it divides. It is located ventral to the esophagus, and its walls are formed by smooth muscle and connective tissue encircled by a series of incomplete horizontal rings of cartilage. The openings in the cartilage rings face the esophagus. Locate the cranial portion of the trachea in the neck region of your cat, and notice the rings of cartilage that support its walls and keep them patent, or open (Figures 5.2 and 5.3).

CAUDAL RESPIRATORY STRUCTURES

The remainder of the respiratory organs are located within the thoracic cavity. To examine them, spread apart the walls of the thorax to observe the thoracic cavity. The respiratory organs within the thoracic cavity are the bronchial tubes and the lungs. Identify these organs, their features, and the structures associated with them.

Bronchi

The trachea terminates in the thoracic cavity dorsal to the heart by dividing into the **right** and **left primary bronchi**, which lead to the lungs (Figure 5.3). Both bronchi include a wall structure similar to the trachea, containing incomplete rings of cartilage. Locate the primary bronchi by gently pushing aside the heart and the cranial lobe of each lung. Once within a lung, the primary bronchus divides into **secondary (lobar) bronchi**, which conduct air to and from individual lobes of the lung. Secondary bronchi branch further to

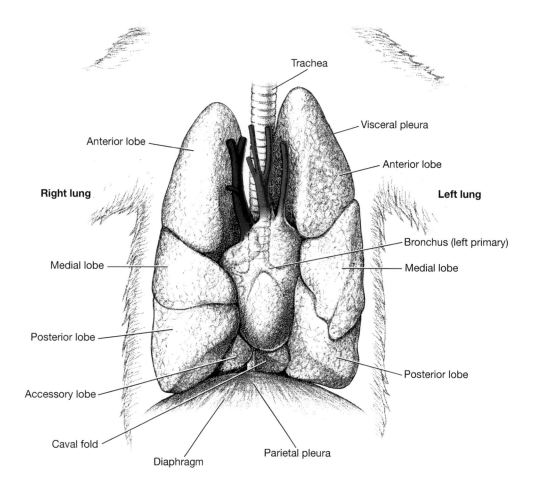

Anterior lobe

Right lung

Medial lobe

Posterior lobe

Accessory lobe

Caval fold

Trachea

Visceral pleura

Anterior lobe

Left lung

Bronchus (left primary)

Medial lobe

Posterior lobe

Diaphragm

Parietal pleura

Figure 5.3 – Caudal respiratory structures

form smaller, **tertiary (segmental) bronchi**, which divide into yet smaller, microscopic **bronchioles**. When combined together, the bronchial branches are referred to as the **bronchial tree**, due to their resemblance to the extensive branching of a tree. The bronchioles terminate directly in **alveolar ducts**, which contain **alveoli**. The microscopic alveoli are the site of gas exchange with the capillaries surrounding them. At this stage of the

dissection procedure, the secondary bronchi and its numerous branches cannot be seen. However, you should be able to observe the primary bronchi by reflecting the lungs medially and picking away tissue surrounding them. The bronchi appear as whitish, shiny tubes.

Pleurae

The pleurae are serous membranes associated with the lungs (Figure 5.3). Two layers of pleura are associated with each lung: the **parietal pleura**, which lines the inner walls of the thoracic cavity; and the **visceral pleura**, which covers the surface of each lung. The space between the pleurae of each lung is called the **pleural cavity**, which in the living cat contains fluid that prevents friction between the two membranes during ventilation. The parietal pleura includes a fold that attaches to the visceral pleura of each lung, called the **pulmonary ligament**. Identify these membranes and compare them with the peritoneal membranes of the abdominal cavity. Their surface appears shiny because of the secretions the cells produce to reduce friction.

Lungs

The lungs are large, multi-lobed structures located lateral, cranial, and caudal to the heart, which lies in the center of the thoracic cavity (Figure 5.3). The lungs are spongy when you squeeze them slightly, which demonstrates their structural composition of many air-filled alveoli. The left lung of the cat includes three lobes: **anterior**, **medial**, and **posterior**. The right lung is divided similarly, except the posterior lobe is subdivided to include an **accessory lobe**. The accessory lobe is tucked into a membrane-enclosed space, called the **caval fold**. The exterior surface of each lung includes a cranial tapering, called the **apex**, and a caudal, concave portion touching the diaphragm called the base. The **mediastinal surface** faces the mediastinum, and the **costal surface** faces the ribcage laterally. The various connections to the lungs include the primary bronchi and blood vessels carrying blood to and from the heart. Combined with the pulmonary ligament, they form the **root** of each lung. Do not cut the root at this time. Located ventral to the root are a pair of white strands, the **phrenic nerves**, which can be observed in the central part of the mediastinum on each side of the pericardial cavity and the heart. These nerves extend to the diaphragm, which they innervate. *The human lungs are similar, except in the number of lobes. The human left lung is divided into two lobes–superior and inferior–and the right lung is divided into three lobes–superior, middle, and inferior.*

CHAPTER REVIEW

A. Answer the following multiple-choice questions by circling the most correct answer.

1. The function of the respiratory system is to
   a. bring oxygen into the bloodstream   b. contract the diaphragm
   c. deliver blood to body tissues   d. rid the body of nitrogenous wastes

2. Together, inspiration and expiration are known as
   a. internal respiration   b. ventilation
   c. external respiration   d. aspiration

3. The internal chamber of the rostrum is called the
   a. choanae   b. nasal cavity
   c. external nares   d. nasal meati

4. A thin, leaf-shaped single cartilage located cranial to the glottis is called the
   a. thyroid cartilage   b. glottis
   c. epiglottis   d. larynx

5. The true vocal cords are located within the
   a. laryngopharynx   b. larynx
   c. glottis   d. trachea

6. The trachea is kept patent, or open, by the presence of
   a. smooth muscle in its walls   b. skeletal muscle contractions
   c. the hyoid bone   d. rings of cartilage in its walls

7. The respiratory organ that is NOT located within the thoracic cavity is the
   a. left lung   b. bronchi
   c. trachea   d. visceral pleura

8. The bronchioles terminate directly in _____, which contain alveoli.
   a. tertiary bronchi   b. alveolar ducts
   c. segmental bronchi   d. alveolar cul-de-sacs

9. The _____ covers the surfaces of each lung.
   a. visceral pericardium   b. parietal pleura
   c. visceral pleura   d. pulmonary ligament

10. The left lung of the cat includes three lobes: anterior, _____, and posterior.
    a. lateral   b. medial
    c. mediastinal   d. dorsal

B. Complete the sentences below by providing the missing terms from the chapter material.

1. The exchange of respiratory gases within the lungs is termed _____ _____.

2. The most important respiratory muscle is the _____.

3. The bronchi and alveoli are located within the _____ cavity.

4. The trachea divides in the chest to form the right and left _____ _____.

5. The nasal cavity is divided by the nasal septum into right and left _____ _____.

6. The _____ _____ is the largest component of the larynx.

7. The junction of the nasopharynx and larynx is marked by an opening called the _____.

8. The site of gas exchange is the microscopic _____ and the capillaries surrounding them.

9. The space between the pleural membranes contains a small amount of fluid, and is called the _____ cavity.

10. The exterior surface of each lung includes a cranial tapering, called the _____, and a caudal, concave portion touching the diaphragm called the base.

C. Answer the following descriptive and critical-thinking questions with a brief explanation in the spaces provided.

1. Describe the process of respiration by including ventilation, internal respiration, and external respiration.

_____

_____

_____

_____

_____

2. Describe the anatomy of the lungs by reviewing the bronchial tree and surrounding structures that form the lungs.

_____

_____

_____

_____

_____

chapter six

THE CIRCULATORY SYSTEM

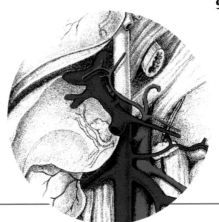

The circulatory system serves as a vital shuttle for the body, transporting substances that include oxygen, carbon dioxide, nutrients, nitrogenous wastes, hormones, and enzymes. Structurally, the circulatory system consists of the centralized pumping organ, the **heart**, and a vast network of blood vessels that carry these substances suspended within the blood. The blood vessels include thick-walled, elastic **arteries**, which carry blood away from the heart, and thin-walled **veins**, which carry blood toward the heart. Interconnecting the arteries and veins are the **capillaries**, which are microscopic vessels with walls so thin (one cell layer) that they are the only site of material exchange between the bloodstream and body cells.

The circulatory system is a closed series of vessels, with the origin and the termination at the heart. It includes two main circulatory networks. The **systemic circulation** is the most extensive, consisting of the arteries and their branches that carry blood away from the left ventricle of the heart, and the veins that return blood to the right atrium of the heart. Its purpose is to transport oxygen-loaded blood to the vicinity of all body cells, with the exception of the lungs, and return oxygen-depleted blood to the heart. The **pulmonary circulation** is the smaller of the two main networks, and consists of the arteries carrying oxygen-depleted blood to the lungs, the extensive vascular branches within the lungs, and the veins that carry oxygen-loaded blood to the left atrium of the heart. The systemic circulation includes the circulatory network of the heart, called the **coronary circulation**, and the circulatory network between the small intestine and the liver, known as the **hepatic portal circulation**.

In this chapter, you will study the organs and associated structures of the circulatory system. The circulatory system of the cat is very typical of mammals, and is surprisingly similar to that of the human. You may assume them to be identical, in fact, unless indicated otherwise. You will begin by examining the heart of the cat and its surrounding structures, followed by the major arteries and veins. During dissection of blood vessels, you will notice that arteries generally lack blood within them, while veins may contain clotted blood. Arteries are under much higher pressure throughout life, while veins carry blood under much lower pressure. The low pressure within the veins allows blood to remain after death, often forming clots.

THE HEART

Your study of the heart begins with a consideration of its external features and the blood vessels connecting directly to it, and ends with the removal of the heart from the thorax and an examination of its internal features.

External Features of the Heart

The heart is located in the thoracic cavity between the two lungs. Partially obscuring it is a large gland with endocrine and lymphatic functions, called the **thymus gland**. Carefully remove the thymus gland, and set it aside for later study. Identify the following external features of the heart:

PERICARDIUM: the two protective layers of serous membrane that surround the heart. The outermost membrane, the **parietal pericardium** or **pericardial sac**, looks like a sack wrapped around the heart (refer to Figures 4.2 and 6.3). Carefully lift the pericardial sac away from the heart surface with forceps and make an incision through it. Continue this incision along the length of the heart and peel the sac away. The space immediately deep to the pericardial sac is the **pericardial cavity**, which in the living cat contains fluid. Immediately deep to the pericardial cavity is the second serous membrane layer, the **visceral pericardium**. This membrane is attached to the underlying cardiac muscle, which forms the walls of the heart. With the pericardial sac peeled way, examine the general shape of the heart. The pointed, caudal end is called the **apex**, and the somewhat flattened, cranial end is the **base**. The two major divisions of the heart can now be identified externally:

VENTRICLES: the large caudal chambers of the heart, which form approximately two-thirds of the heart's bulk (Figure 6.1). Internally, they are completely separated into a **right** and a **left ventricle**. This separation is represented on the external surface by a shallow groove called the **interventricular sulcus**. Fat and **coronary blood vessels** can be seen within this sulcus.

ATRIA: the smaller cranial chambers of the heart. The **right** and **left atria**, also separated internally, are divided from each other externally by some of the large vessels that unite with the heart. The atria are externally separated from the ventricles by a fat-filled groove called the **coronal sulcus**, which encircles the heart (Figure 6.1). Clear away the fat in this sulcus and locate the coronary blood vessels that pass through it. The externally attached, ear-shaped projection of each atrium is known as the **auricle**, or **auricular appendage**.

Blood Vessels of the Heart

You are now ready to study the major blood vessels of the heart. Most preserved specimens have had colored material (usually latex) injected into some of their vessels after death. This color-coding distinguishes between arteries and veins and makes the blood vessels tougher and more elastic. Doubly injected specimens have a red material in the arteries and a blue material in the veins. In

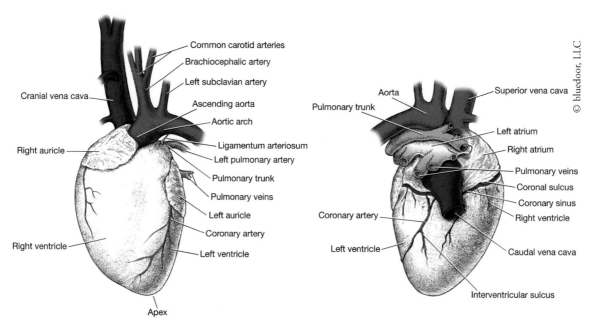

Figure 6.1 – External features of the heart (left ventral view, right dorsal view).

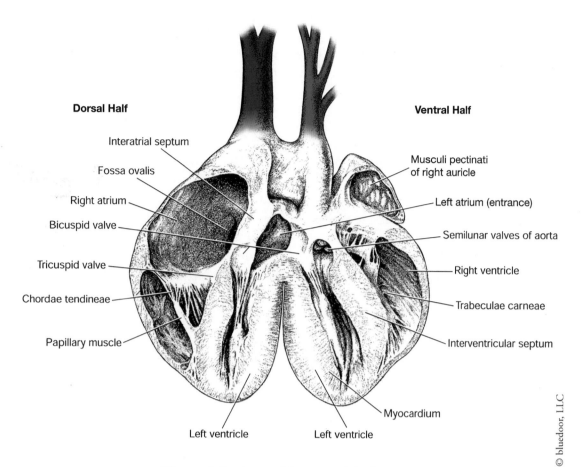

Dorsal Half

Interatrial septum

Fossa ovalis

Right atrium

Bicuspid valve

Tricuspid valve

Chordae tendineae

Papillary muscle

Left ventricle

Ventral Half

Musculi pectinati of right auricle

Left atrium (entrance)

Semilunar valves of aorta

Right ventricle

Trabeculae carneae

Interventricular septum

Myocardium

Left ventricle

© bluedoor, LLC

Figure 6.2 – Internal features of the heart.

triply injected specimens, a yellow (or occasionally a green) material is injected into the hepatic portal system. With this color coding in mind, examine the large vessels on the ventral side of the heart (Figure 6.1).

PULMONARY TRUNK: a wide vessel that arises from the right ventricle. If injected, the pulmonary trunk is blue, even though it carries blood away from the heart. Frequently, however, it is not injected. Observe that it emerges between the right and left atria.

Pulmonary arteries: cranial to the heart, the pulmonary trunk bifurcates (divides) into a right and left pulmonary artery, each of which extends dorsally to its prospective lung. These arteries carry deoxygenated blood to the lungs.

AORTA: located dorsal to the pulmonary trunk, the aorta is the large, wide vessel that emerges from the left ventricle. It ascends from its ori-gin (**ascending aorta**), forms a prominent arch as it curves dorsally (**aortic arch**), then descends behind the heart caudally to the diaphragm (**descending aorta**). At this point in the dissection procedure, you will be able to identify only the ascending aorta and the aortic arch. Before descending, this thick-walled artery gives off four major branches:

Coronary arteries: paired vessels that originate from the base of the aorta and extend to the heart wall. Running parallel to these arteries in the heart sulci, **coronary veins** drain the heart wall. The main drainage vessel of the heart wall is the **coronary sinus**, a large vein in the coronary sulcus.

Brachiocephalic artery: a single, large vessel that is the first major branch to arise from the arch of the aorta. It continues in a cranial direction until it divides into three vessels: **two common carotid**

arteries and the **right subclavian artery**, both of which will be traced later.

Left subclavian artery: a single artery arising from the aortic arch lateral to the brachiocephalic artery. It passes to the left shoulder and supplies the left pectoral appendages and left ventral body wall with oxygenated blood.

VENA CAVAE: two large veins that drain blood from the systemic circulatory network into the right atrium. Push the heart of your cat to the left side of the thorax and note that the vena cavae enter the right atrium on the dorsal side. Do not attempt to view the entire dorsal side of the heart at this time; you will study it after the heart has been removed from the thoracic cavity.

Cranial vena cava: a large vein that drains the body cranial to the heart. It unites with the aright atrium at its cranial surface.

Caudal vena cava: a large vein that drains the body caudal to the heart. Arising from the union of the common iliac veins in the pelvic region, it enters the caudal surface of the right atrium.

Internal Features of the Heart

Cut the large vessels associated with the heart that you just identified no closer than 1 cm (½ inch) from their union with the heart. Remove the heart from the thoracic cavity, and again identify the heart chambers and large vessels on the ventral side. Carefully clean the dorsal surface of the heart, and identify the chambers and vessels on that side, as well. Note particularly the **pulmonary veins**, which were not visible ventrally. Passing from the lungs, these four veins carry oxygen-rich blood into the left atrium.

To study the internal anatomy of the heart, first make an incision through the transverse plane of the heart wall beginning at the apex and continuing upward until the two ventricles are completely exposed. Next, open the right atrium by making an incision from its auricle into the caudal vena cava, and open the left atrium by making an incision from its auricle through one of the pulmonary veins. If the heart chambers are filled with latex, remove it carefully to avoid damage to the heart valves. Then locate each of the following structures and identify their associated features (Figure 6.2):

RIGHT ATRIUM: the thin-walled cranial chamber on the right side, which is formed by the union of the vena cavae. It also receives the coronary sinus, which encircles the heart wall. Note the smooth internal surface of this chamber. Also notice the presence of muscular ridges on the auricular walls; they are known as **musculi pectinati**. A slight depression may be noticeable near the entrance of the caudal vena cava. The depression, called the **fossa ovalis**, represents the location of an opening between the two atria that was present before birth (called the foramen ovale), which served as a shunt for blood to bypass the lungs during fetal development.

LEFT ATRIUM: the thin-walled cranial chamber on the left side that receives the four pulmonary veins. It is separated from the right atrium by a thin, muscular partition called the **interatrial septum**.

ATRIOVENTRICULAR (AV) VALVES: one-way valves located between the atrium and ventricle of each side. The **right atrioventricular valve**, or **tricuspid valve**, consists of three flap-like cusps, which direct blood to flow from the right atrium to the right ventricle. The **left atrioventricular valve**, or **bicuspid valve**, consists of two cusps that direct blood to flow from the left atrium to the left ventricle. The downward-pointing apex of each cusp is connected to one or more thin, white strands of connective tissue, called **chordae tendineae**, which attach to small muscles that project from the ventricular walls. The muscles are known as **papillary muscles**, and serve to keep the cords tight to prevent inversion of the valves into the atria during ventricular contraction. *The bicuspid valve is alternatively called the mitral valve in the human heart.*

SEMILUNAR (SL) VALVES: one-way valves located between the ventricles and the two major arteries emerging from the heart. Each semilunar valve consists of three pocket-shaped cusps located at the base of each vessel. The valve in the pulmonary trunk is also called the **pulmonary valve**, and that in the aorta is the **aortic valve**.

- **RIGHT VENTRICLE**: the thick-walled, caudal chamber on the right side of the heart. It receives oxygen-depleted blood from the right atrium through the tricuspid valve, and pushes blood through the pulmonary valve to flow into the pulmonary trunk and circulation.

- **LEFT VENTRICLE**: the large, thick-walled caudal chamber on the left side of the heart. Its muscular wall, called the **myocardium**, is thicker than that of the right ventricle, due to its requirement of pushing oxygen-refreshed blood through the aortic valve and into the aorta to circulate through the extensive systemic circulation. The left and right ventricles are separated internally by a thick-walled partition called the **interventricular septum**. Also, notice the muscular ridges throughout the inner walls of both ventricles. These ridges are called **trabeculae carneae**.

SYSTEMIC BLOOD VESSELS

The blood vessels that form the systemic circuit are studied next. You have already identified the major branches of the pulmonary circuit, due to their union and close proximity to the heart. The systemic vessels are divided into cranial blood vessels and caudal blood vessels, using the heart as the central reference point. Arteries, colored in red latex, are described as they extend away from the heart. Veins, colored in blue latex, are described as they travel toward the heart. As you dissect the blood vessels, you should keep in mind that they vary considerably between specimens; presented in this manual is the most common circulatory pattern. Also, arteries and veins tend to share similar pathways through the body, often running in parallel. Therefore, these vessels share a common name, which usually corresponds to the region they supply or pass through.

Blood Vessels Cranial to the Heart

The systemic blood vessels located cranial to the heart supply the brain, upper limbs, and thoracic cavity with oxygen-refreshed blood and drain oxygen-depleted blood into the right atrium of the heart. You will begin your study with the aortic tributaries, tracing the major arterial branches as they run further from the heart. Then you will trace the cranial veins from their peripheral origins to the right atrium.

To begin, locate the aortic arch once again. Note its major branches are the large **brachiocephalic artery** and the smaller **left subclavian artery** (Figures 6.3 and 6.4). The brachiocephalic artery gives rise to the **left common carotid artery**, then to the **right common carotid artery**, and finally to the **right subclavian artery**. *In the human, the aortic arch branching pattern is different. The brachiocephalic artery gives rise to the right common carotid artery and right subclavian artery, while the left common carotid artery and the left subclavian artery arise independently from the aortic arch.* Trace the following branches of the common carotid arteries, then the subclavian arteries:

- **COMMON CAROTID ARTERIES**: large paired arteries that extend cranially to supply the head and neck regions. From the common carotid, the **external carotid artery** passes cranially through the parotid salivary gland on each side of the head to supply structures of the head and neck. The external carotid is a cranial continuation of the common carotid, and begins at the level of the jaw where the small **internal carotid artery** arises. From each side, its major tributaries include the **lingual artery**, which passes ventrally to supply the tongue; the **facial artery**, which supplies the jaws and facial structures (both tributaries actually originate at a common point on a cranial continuation of the external carotid called the **linguofacial artery**); and a **maxillary artery**, which supplies the masseter muscle.

- **SUBCLAVIAN ARTERIES**: pass laterally to the shoulder region. The **right subclavian artery** originates from the division of the brachiocephalic and passes to the right shoulder to

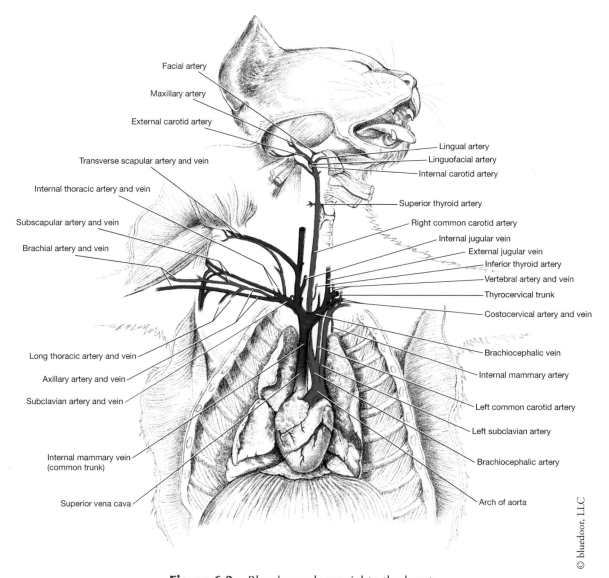

Facial artery

Maxillary artery

External carotid artery

Transverse scapular artery and vein

Internal thoracic artery and vein

Subscapular artery and vein

Brachial artery and vein

Lingual artery

Linguofacial artery

Internal carotid artery

Superior thyroid artery

Right common carotid artery

Internal jugular vein

External jugular vein

Inferior thyroid artery

Vertebral artery and vein

Thyrocervical trunk

Costocervical artery and vein

Long thoracic artery and vein

Axillary artery and vein

Subclavian artery and vein

Brachiocephalic vein

Internal mammary artery

Left common carotid artery

Left subclavian artery

Brachiocephalic artery

Internal mammary vein
(common trunk)

Superior vena cava

Arch of aorta

Figure 6.3 – Blood vessels cranial to the heart.

become the **right axillary artery**. The **left subclavian artery** arises directly from the aortic arch, extends cranially, and turns toward the left shoulder to become the **left axillary artery**. From both subclavian arteries branch the **vertebral artery**, which passes to the brain, where it becomes the **basilar artery**; the **internal thoracic artery**, which supplies the ventral chest wall; the **costocervical artery**, which supplies the intercostal muscles in the cranial region of the chest; and the **thyrocervical artery**, whose tributaries pass to the thyroid gland and the scapular muscles.

AXILLARY ARTERIES: a continuation of the subclavian arteries into the armpit (axilla) region on each side. Branching from each axillary artery are numerous smaller arteries supplying the muscles of the shoulder, chest, and upper limb regions.

BRACHIAL ARTERIES: a continuation of the axillary arteries of both sides as they enter the brachium. Along the length of each brachial artery branch numerous smaller arteries that supply the muscles of the brachium, the most prominent of which is the **deep brachial artery**.

RADIAL ARTERIES: at the elbow region of each upper limb, the brachial artery continues distally as the radial artery, which extends to the pes. Midway through the ante-

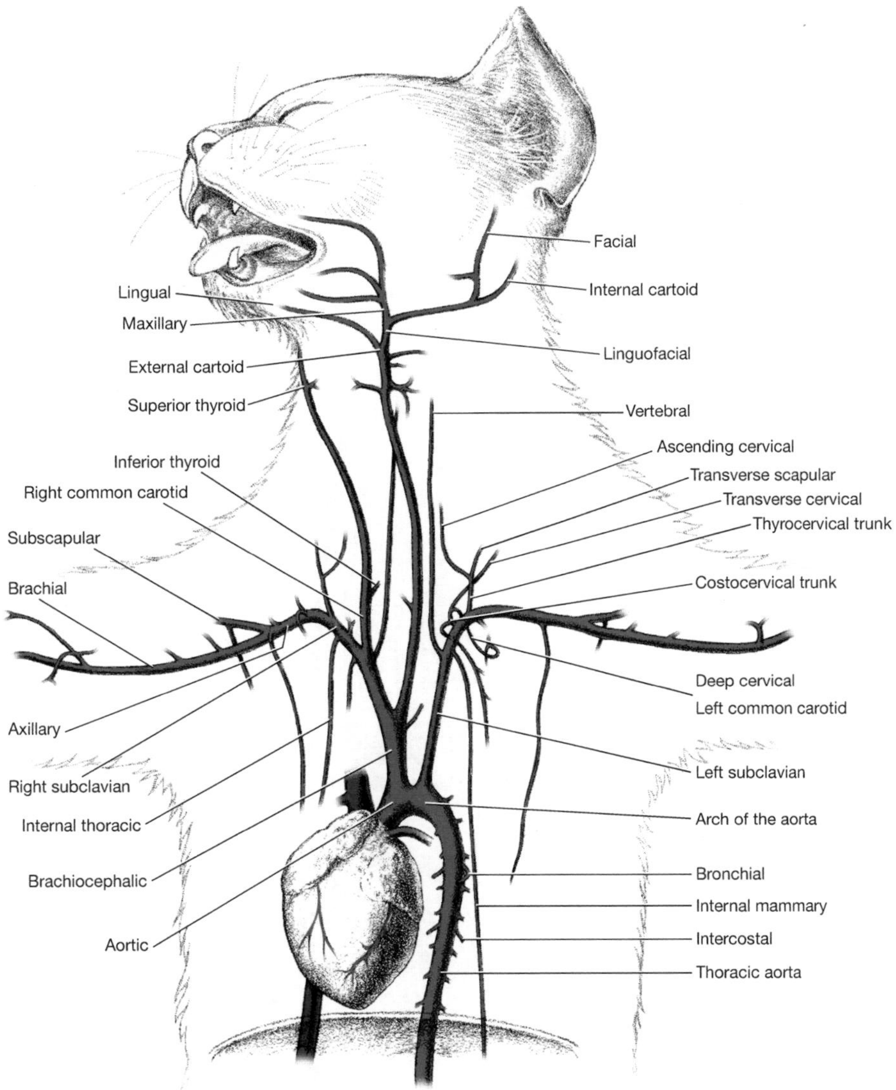
Facial
Internal cartoid
Lingual
Maxillary
Linguofacial
External cartoid
Superior thyroid
Vertebral
Ascending cervical
Inferior thyroid
Transverse scapular
Right common carotid
Transverse cervical
Thyrocervical trunk
Subscapular
Brachial
Costocervical trunk
Deep cervical
Left common carotid
Axillary
Left subclavian
Right subclavian
Internal thoracic
Arch of the aorta
Brachiocephalic
Bronchial
Internal mammary
Intercostal
Aortic
Thoracic aorta
© bluedoor, LLC

Figure 6.4 – Schematic view of artieries cranial to the heart.

THE CIRCULATORY SYSTEM

brachium, the radial artery gives rise to a major branch, the **ulnar artery**.

The next step in your dissection of cranial blood vessels is to identify the cranial veins. Most peripheral veins parallel the arteries with which they share a common name, but there are some notable exceptions as the veins approach the heart. Locate the following major cranial veins in your cat, which you will trace according to the flow of venous blood toward the heart (Figures 6.3 and 6.5). Note that they carry blood to the cranial vena cava, which empties into the right atrium.

INTERNAL JUGULAR VEINS: formed by the union of veins that drain structures lying within the cranial cavity, it exits the cranial cavity through the jugular foramen and descends to the lower neck region, traveling medial to the larger external jugular vein on each side. It usually unites with the external jugular cranial to the junction between the subclavian and cranial vena cava.

EXTERNAL JUGULAR VEINS: large, superficial veins on each side of the neck. They extend caudally until they merge to form the cranial vena cava. Uniting with the external jugular is the **transverse scapular vein**, which joins the external jugular just cranial to its

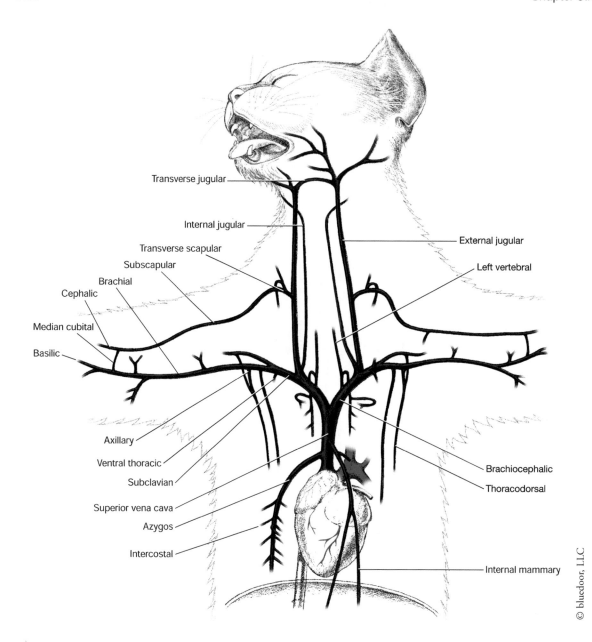

Transverse jugular

Internal jugular

Transverse scapular

Subscapular

Brachial

Cephalic

Median cubital

Basilic

Axillary

Ventral thoracic

Subclavian

Superior vena cava

Azygos

Intercostal

External jugular

Left vertebral

Brachiocephalic

Thoracodorsal

Internal mammary

© bluedoor, LLC

Figure 6.5 – Schematic view of veins cranial to the heart.

union with the internal jugular vein, and drains the deep shoulder region. In the cranial neck, the external jugulars from both sides are bridged by the **transverse jugular vein**.

BRACHIAL VEINS: a large vein in the brachium of each upper limb. Each is formed as a cranial continuation of the **basilic vein** in the antebrachium. At the union of the basilic and brachial veins is the **median cubital vein**, which travels transversely to unite with the **subscapular vein** in the brachium. The sub-

scapular vein is a cranial continuation of the superficial **cephalic vein** in the antebrachium.

AXILLARY VEINS: a continuation of the brachial veins on each side in the axilla region. Its tributaries correspond to those of the axillary arteries.

SUBCLAVIAN VEINS: a continuation of the axillary veins in each shoulder, they extend medially to unite with the cranial vena cava at the level of the first rib. The subclavians drain the pectoral region.

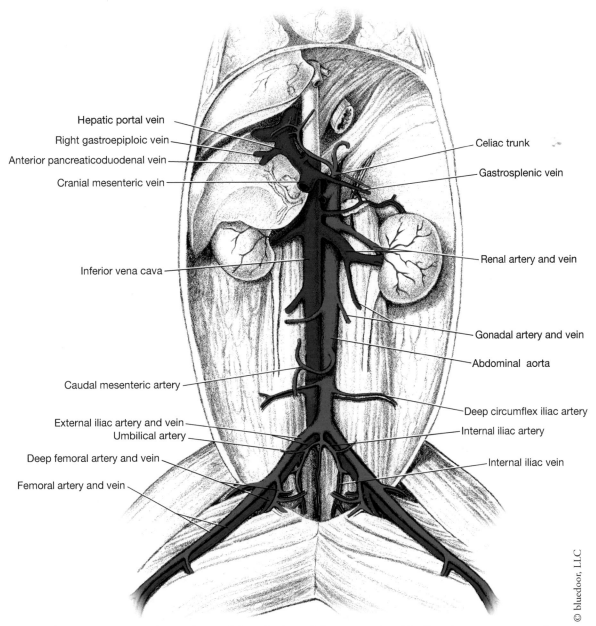

Hepatic portal vein
Right gastroepiploic vein
Anterior pancreaticoduodenal vein
Cranial mesenteric vein

Celiac trunk
Gastrosplenic vein

Inferior vena cava

Renal artery and vein

Gonadal artery and vein
Abdominal aorta

Caudal mesenteric artery

Deep circumflex iliac artery
Internal iliac artery

External iliac artery and vein
Umbilical artery

Internal iliac vein

Deep femoral artery and vein

Femoral artery and vein

© bluedoor, LLC

Figure 6.6 – Blood vessels caudal to the heart (deep vessels with digestive tract removed).

BRACHIOCEPHALIC VEINS: large veins formed by the union of the external jugular veins and subclavian veins on each side, they merge above the heart to form the cranial vena cava. Note the **azygos vein** and **internal mammary vein**, both of which unite with the cranial vena cava shortly before it merges with the right atrium.

Blood Vessels Caudal to the Heart

The arteries caudal to the heart are tributaries of the **descending aorta**, the section of the aorta that extends downward through the thoracic and abdominal cavities, where it is called the **thoracic aorta** and **abdominal aorta**, respectively. Trace the path of this vessel from its origin at the aortic arch, along the dorsal wall of the thorax, through the **aortic hiatus** in the diaphragm, and along the abdominal wall. Note that it is located behind the peritoneum. Identify the following tributaries of the descending aorta, working from cranial to caudal (Figures 6.6 and 6.7):

CELIAC TRUNK: a large, single artery that is the cranial-most branch from the descending aorta below the diaphragm. To observe it, push the abdominal viscera to the right and locate the area where the aorta emerges from the diaphragm. The celiac arises from the aorta immediately below the aortic hiatus. Its branches include the **left gastric artery**, which passes to the stomach; the **hepatic artery**, which supplies the liver, part of the stomach, the duodenum, the pancreas, and the spleen via smaller branches; and the **splenic artery**, which supplies part of the stomach, the spleen, the pancreas, and the greater omentum.

CRANIAL MESENTERIC ARTERY: arising from the descending aorta just caudal to the origin of the celiac trunk, it is a large, single artery supplying the pancreas, small intestine, and large intestine via its smaller branches.

ADRENOLUMBAR ARTERY: arising from the descending aorta caudal to the origin of the cranial mesenteric, it supplies the adrenal gland and lumbar muscles.

RENAL ARTERIES: paired arteries that course from the aorta laterally to supply the right and left kidneys.

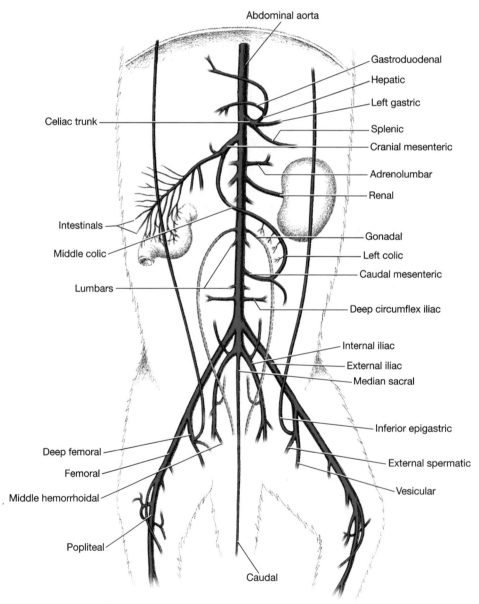

© bluedoor, LLC

Figure 6.7 – Schematic view of arteries caudal to the heart.

GONADAL ARTERIES: paired arteries that emerge from the aorta caudal to the renals. They are called the **testicular arteries** in the male, and supply the testes, scrotum, and penis. In the female, they are the **ovarian arteries,** and supply the ovaries and uterus.

CAUDAL MESENTERIC ARTERY: arising from the descending aorta, this single artery courses ventrally toward the large intestine, which it supplies.

LUMBAR ARTERIES: seven pairs of smaller arteries arising from the aorta in the lower back region, which course laterally between the dorsal musculature to supply them and the spinal cord.

DEEP CIRCUMFLEX ILIAC ARTERIES: paired vessels that course laterally from their origin with the aorta. They supply the abdominal wall.

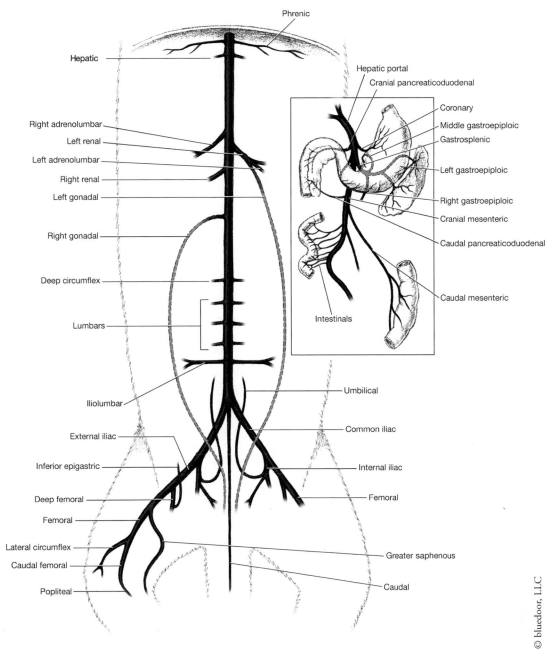

Figure 6.8 – Schematic view of veins caudal to the heart and the hepatic portal system (insert).

EXTERNAL ILIAC ARTERIES: with the large intestine and urinary bladder pushed aside, you'll be able to identify the external iliacs as paired arteries emerging from the aorta at the level of the sacrum. Each extends to a hindlimb, which it supplies. Just before each external iliac emerges through the body wall from the pelvic cavity, it gives off a **deep femoral artery**, which supplies the urinary bladder, external genitalia, and several thigh muscles by way of its branches. *Note that there are no common iliac arteries, which are prominent in the human systemic circulation.*

INTERNAL ILIAC ARTERIES: the last pair of arteries to arise from the descending aorta. After their emergence, the aorta continues a short distance as the **median sacral artery** along the dorsal aspect of the pelvic cavity, and as the **caudal artery** along the ventral aspect and into the tail.

Return to the external iliac arteries, and trace their tributaries that extend into the hindlimbs. Identify these vessels from the following descriptions:

FEMORAL ARTERIES: as each external iliac artery begins its journey down the medial surface of a leg, its name changes to femoral artery when it emerges from the body wall. The femoral artery continues down the thigh, where it gives off the **lateral circumflex artery**, supplying the quadriceps muscle group, sartorius, and tensor fascia latae. About midway down the thigh, it gives off a second tributary, the **saphenous artery**, which courses superficially to the medial surface of the thigh and shank. Near the knee, the femoral artery gives off the **articular artery**, which supplies the gracilis, semimembranosus, and vastus lateralis muscles.

POPLITEAL ARTERIES: the femoral artery extends to the knee, passing between muscles to become the popliteal artery behind the kneecap. The popliteal artery supplies muscles of the shank, foot, and thigh by way of its branches.

The next step in your dissection of caudal blood vessels is to identify the caudal veins. Locate the following major caudal veins in your cat, which you will trace according to the flow of venous blood toward the heart (Figure 6.8):

POPLITEAL VEINS: paralleling the popliteal arteries in the popliteal fossa behind the kneecap, the popliteal veins of both hind limbs course in a cranial direction to become the femoral vein as they enter the thigh musculature. The popliteal veins drain the shank and pes by way of smaller veins that converge to form the popliteals.

FEMORAL VEINS: a prominent vein of each hind limb that courses through the thigh musculature. Each is formed by the union of smaller **caudal femoral veins** that emerge from the popliteal veins, and the **lateral circumflex femoral vein**. The major tributary of each femoral vein is the **greater saphenous vein**, which parallels the greater saphenous artery along the medial surface of the thigh and shank. The **deep femoral vein** also unites with the femoral vein.

EXTERNAL ILIAC VEINS: large veins coursing parallel to the external iliac arteries. Soon after the external iliacs enter the pelvic cavity, they merge with the smaller **internal iliac veins** to form the **common iliac veins**, which in turn merge to form the caudal vena cava.

Once formed by the union of the common iliac veins from both sides, the caudal vena cava extends cranially and gradually increases in diameter to accommodate the increased blood flow resulting from the confluence of other tributaries. Now trace the major veins that unite with the caudal vena cava, which parallel the arteries sharing similar names. Once you've completed this task, identify the hepatic portal vein and the veins draining into it, as described below and illustrated in Figure 6.8.

ILIOLUMBAR VEINS: paired veins that unite with the caudal vena cava near its formation from the external· iliacs, which drain structures in the lumbar region.

LUMBAR VEINS: several pairs of small veins that unite with the caudal vena cava cranial to its origin in the lumbar region. They drain the lumbar muscles.

DEEP CIRCUMFLEX ILIAC VEINS: a pair of veins that unite with the caudal vena cava in the upper lumbar region.

GONADAL VEINS: called the **testicular veins** in the male and **ovarian veins** in the female, they course parallel to the arteries of the same name.

RENAL VEINS: a pair of veins that carry blood from each kidney to the caudal vena cava, and parallel the renal arteries.

ADRENOLUMBAR VEINS: paired veins that drain the adrenal glands and lumbar structures into the caudal vena cava.

HEPATIC VEIN: a single, large vein that drains blood from the liver into the caudal vena cava. To view it, reflect the lobes of the liver that surround the caudal vena cava.

HEPATIC PORTAL VEIN: a single, prominent vein that does not unite with the caudal vena cava. It shunts blood from the abdominal viscera, especially the small intestine, to the liver for processing newly absorbed nutrients. The **hepatic portal vein** receives blood from numerous veins, which form the hepatic portal system. A portal system shunts blood from one capillary network to another, whereas a normal venous system carries blood from a capillary network toward the heart. The hepatic portal system can be seen by pushing aside the abdominal visceral organs, since much of it lies within the mesentery proper and the lesser omentum. In some specimen, the hepatic portal system has been injected with yellow latex, making it easier to study. The major veins that channel blood to the hepatic portal vein include the **coronary vein**, which drains the lesser curvature of the stomach; a **right gastroepiploic vein**, which drains most of the stomach wall; the **cranial pancreaticoduodenal vein**, which drains the duodenum and pancreas; the **gastrosplenic vein**, which receives blood from the stomach, spleen, and pancreas; the **caudal pancreaticoduodenal vein**, which drains blood from the pancreas and the duodenum into the cranial mesenteric vein; the **caudal mesenteric vein**, which drains blood from the large intestine to also join the **cranial mesenteric vein**; and the cranial mesenteric vein, which drains blood from the small intestine, transverse and ascending colon, and part of the pancreas directly into the hepatic portal vein. *The human hepatic portal circulation is similar to that of the cat, with one major exception: the hepatic portal vein of the human is formed by the convergence of the superior mesenteric vein (cranial mesenteric vein of the cat) and the splenic vein (the gastrosplenic vein of the cat).*

LYMPHATIC ORGANS AND CIRCULATION

The lymphatic organs are often considered part of the circulatory system in an anatomical study. However, they may also be categorized as a separate system, the **lymphatic system**, when the cardiovascular system is considered apart from the circulatory system and function is emphasized. Because our study of the cat is anatomical, we will consider the lymphatic organs in this discussion.

The lymphatic organs play two roles: rechanneling fluid that is lost during capillary exchange to the bloodstream, and engaging a defense against infectious disease. The rechanneling of fluid is provided by a series of vessels, called **lymphatic vessels**, that transport lymph from its origin in tissues toward the heart. Lymph is formed as interstitial fluid enters blind-ended lymphatic capillaries, which are located in nearly all tissues near blood capillaries. The lymph is carried through lymphatic vessels, which usually parallel veins and are similar in structure. However, because the lymphatic vessels are usually not colored with latex, their almost transparent structure is extremely difficult to observe in a dissection.

The lymphatic vessels drain lymph into one of two main collecting trunks. The **thoracic duct** drains lymph from all tissues caudal to the heart and the left cranial side of the body. It parallels the descending aorta in the thoracic cavity, and may be observed by examining the dorsal thoracic

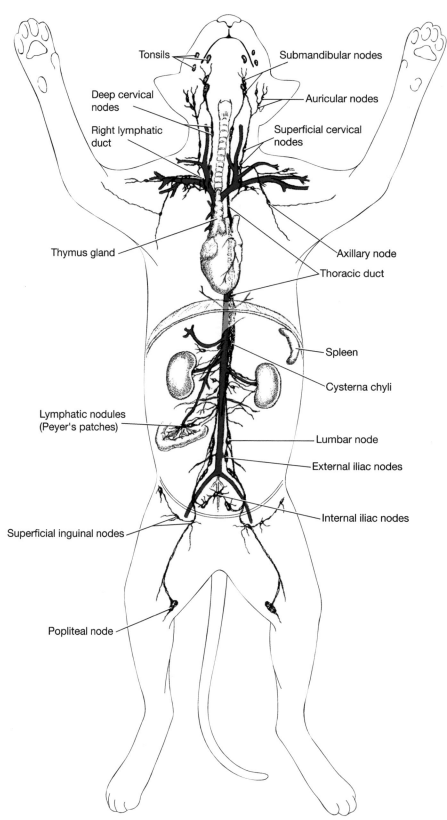

Figure 6.9 – The lymphatic system of the cat (the kidneys, heart, trachea, vessels, and diaphragm are included to provide reference of location).

wall. The thoracic duct drains lymph into the left subclavian vein, thereby returning the fluid to the bloodstream. The right cranial side of the body is drained by the **right lymphatic duct**, which is a very short vessel less than ½ cm in the cat. It drains lymph into the right subclavian vein.

As lymph is carried toward the heart, it passes through numerous **lymph nodes**. These small oval structures receive lymph from several afferent lymphatic vessels, then release it through a single efferent lymphatic vessel. Lymph nodes contain many lymphocytes, which react to infectious materials by destroying them by several means. As a result, the lymph is filtered of unwanted pathogens and their byproducts.

Other lymphatic organs include the tonsils, spleen, thymus gland, and lymphatic nodules, known as Peyer's patches, associated with the intestines. The tonsils include the **palatine tonsils** located within the palatoglossal fossae bordering the fauces, the **pharyngeal tonsils** located in the nasopharynx, and the **lingual tonsils** located at the base of the tongue. The tonsils are also composed of lymphocytes.

You have previously observed the **spleen**, which is located laterodorsal to the stomach within the abdominal cavity. The spleen contains lymphocytes, and also includes large modified veins that store red blood cells.

The **thymus gland** was described previously in this chapter, due to its location within the thoracic cavity cranial to the heart. It was removed in order to observe the heart. The thymus gland provides a site for lymphocyte development, which is most active immediately after birth. It also produces a hormone, thymosin, and is thereby considered an endocrine gland, as well as a lymphatic organ.

The **lympatic nodules**, or Peyer's patches, are clusters of lymphocytes in the outers walls of the small and large intestines. They participate in controlling the migration of microorganisms out of the GI tract, and prevent them from entering the bloodstream to cause infection. They are not visible from a gross dissection.

The lymphatic system of the cat is diagrammed in Figure 6.9 for your reference and study.

CHAPTER REVIEW

A. Answer the following multiple-choice questions by circling the most correct answer.

1. The blood vessels that carry blood away from the heart are known as
   a. arteries
   b. veins
   c. capillaries
   d. none of the above

2. The circulatory route that transports blood to and from the lungs is the
   a. systemic circulation
   b. pulmonary circulation
   c. coronary circulation
   d. hepatic portal circulation

3. The sack-like structure that contains the heart is known as the
   a. visceral pericardium
   b. parietal pleura
   c. pericardial sac
   d. mediastinum

4. The heart chamber that receives the vena cavae is the
   a. right ventricle
   b. left ventricle
   c. right atrium
   d. left atrium

5. The large vessel that carries blood away from the left ventricle is called the
   a. pulmonary trunk
   b. aorta
   c. cranial vena cava
   d. coronary vein

6. The first major vessel to arise from the arch of the aorta is the
   a. coronary artery
   b. brachiocephalic artery
   c. right subclavian artery
   d. common carotid artery

7. The right semilunar valve is located
   a. within the right ventricle
   b. at the origin of the pulmonary trunk
   c. at the origin of the aorta
   d. between the right atrium and right ventricle

8. You should be able to observe the interventricular septum by viewing the
   a. sectioned heart
   b. upper thoracic cavity
   c. inside of the right atrium
   d. external surface of the heart

9. The femoral artery arises from the
   a. abdominal aorta
   b. external iliac artery
   c. external carotid artery
   d. popliteal artery

10. Lymph may be found within
   a. blood vessels
   b. the spleen
   c. the thoracic duct
   d. the left ventricle

B. Complete the sentences below by providing the missing terms from the chapter material.

1. The exchange of materials occurs by diffusion across the walls of _____.

2. The bicuspid valve directs blood to flow from the left atrium to the _____ _____.

3. The fossa ovalis is located in the wall of the _____ _____.

4. The _____ _____ gives rise to the left common carotid artery, then to the right common carotid artery, and finally to the right subclavian artery.

5. The _____ _____ _____ is a large vein that drains the body caudal to the heart.

6. Chordae tendineae may be found within the _____.

7. The large, superficial veins on each side of the neck are called _____ _____ ____.

8. At the elbow region of each upper limb, the brachial artery continues distally as the _____ _____, which extends to the pes.

9. The large, single artery that is the cranial-most branch from the descending aorta below the diaphragm is called the _____ _____.

10. A single, prominent vein that does not unite with the caudal vena cava and shunts blood from the abdominal viscera, especially the small intestine, to the liver for processing newly absorbed nutrients, describes the _____ _____ _____.

C. Answer the following descriptive and critical-thinking questions with a brief explanation in the spaces provided.

1. Describe the flow of blood through the heart in proper sequence; include the heart valves and heart chambers.

_____

_____

_____

_____

_____

2. What is a portal circulation, and how does the hepatic portal system meet this definition?

_____

_____

_____

_____

_____

_____

3. Identify the major branches of the aorta described in the text. _____

_____

_____

_____

_____

_____

_____

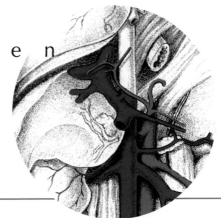

c h a p t e r   s e v e n

THE UROGENITAL SYSTEM

The urogenital system combines two systems, the urinary system and the reproductive system. The two systems are combined in this chapter because of the close anatomical relationship between them, which is common among mammals. As you will soon discover, several urinary organs lie in direct contact with reproductive organs, and in some cases, the functions of both systems take place within a common organ. The overall functions of the two systems are quite distinct, however.

The primary function of the urinary system is the formation of urine, which achieves several roles: the removal of nitrogen-containing materials that result from metabolic activities; the management of the water and salt balance of body fluids; and the regulation of blood pressure. Urine formation occurs in the kidneys, at the site of functional subunits called **nephrons**. Within the nephrons, blood is filtered, water is reabsorbed back into the bloodstream, and unwanted ions are secreted, resulting in a waste fluid known as urine. The remaining organs of the urinary system channel urine to the body's exterior. They are the ureters, urinary bladder, and urethra.

In contrast to urinary functions, the reproductive system performs the role of procreation. The system is unique in that the male and female structures are very different from each other, and are therefore said to exhibit **sexual dimorphism**. In the female, the reproductive organs are highly adapted for the production of the female gametes (**ova**) and for the internal fertilization process, the internal incubation of the developing embryo and fetus, and the birth process. In the male, reproductive organs are adapted for the production of the male gametes (**spermatozoa**) and for the internal semination process.

In this chapter, you will examine the urogenital system of the cat through dissection. The chapter begins with a study of the urinary system. Then, you will study the reproductive systems, including that of both sexes.

THE URINARY SYSTEM

With your cat specimen lying on its dorsal side, locate the following organs and features of the urinary system. The urinary organs include the kidneys, ureters, urinary bladder, and urethra.

Kidneys

The kidneys are bean-shaped organs that lie partially embedded in fat against the dorsal body wall (Figures 7.1, 7.2, and 7.3). To observe them, you must first push the visceral digestive organs completely to one side. If you are dissecting on a wax tray, pin these organs to the tray for the remainder of your study of the urogenital system. Note that the kidneys are not suspended within the abdominal cavity, as are the visceral digestive organs, but lie outside the parietal peritoneum. This positioning is called **retroperitoneal**. Also note the position of the **adrenal glands**, which lie slightly cranial and medial to each kidney.

Carefully remove the fat from one of the kidneys, section it along the frontal plane, and identify the following features (Figure 7.1).

RENAL FASCIA: the outer layer of connective tissue that anchors each kidney to the dorsal abdominal wall.

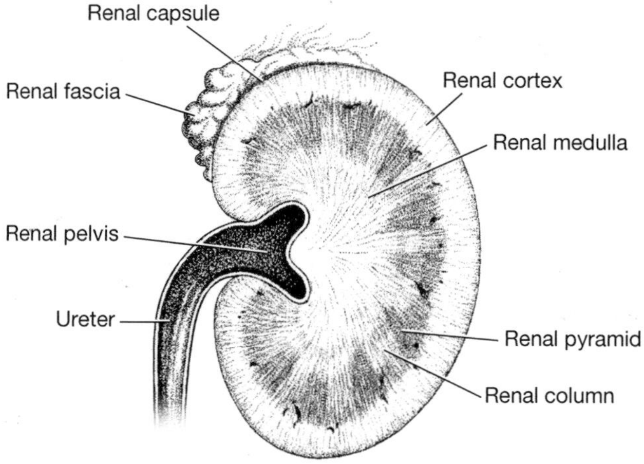

Figure 7.1 – Kidney (sectioned along the
frontal plane).

RENAL CAPSULE: a thin layer of transparent fibrous connective tissue that encloses each kidney and is deep to the renal fascia.

HILUM: a depression near the center of each kidney's concave medial border through which the renal artery, renal vein, lymphatic vessels, and nerves enter or exit.

RENAL PELVIS: a membrane-lined basin in the center of each kidney, which unites with the mucous membrane lining the ureter. Along its borders are cup-like extensions known as calyces, including major and minor. The calyces receive newly formed urine and channel it into the center of the renal pelvis.

RENAL CORTEX: the outermost region of the kidney. It is relatively smooth in texture, and outlines the internal periphery. The renal cortex extends from the renal capsule to the internal region of the kidney, the medulla (described next). The cortex is composed of blood vessels and renal corpuscles (ball-shaped components of nephrons that contain the filtration apparatus).

RENAL MEDULLA: the inner region of the kidney parenchyma. It includes from six to eighteen triangular, striated structures called **renal pyramids**. The bases of the pyramids face the renal cortex, and the apices, or renal papillae, point to the renal pelvis. The areas between adjacent renal pyramids are called **renal columns**. The renal medulla is composed of blood vessels and renal tubules (lengths of tubes that form part of the nephron).

Ureters

The paired ureters are narrow tubes that transport urine from the hili of the kidneys to the urinary bladder at the base of the pelvic cavity (Figures 7.2 and 7.3). Each ureter arises from the renal pelvis of a kidney, and courses caudally in a retroperitoneal pathway until it unites with the dorsal wall of the bladder. Along the surface of each ureter is a thin layer of fibrous connective tissue that is continuous with the renal capsule of a kidney. Carefully pick away any remaining connective tissue and fat covering one of the ureters to expose it. In males, another small tube, the vas deferens, coils around the ureter near the base of the urinary bladder; avoid damaging the vas deferens for later study.

Urinary Bladder

Follow the path of the ureters to their caudal extremities. Here they unite with the sac-like uri-

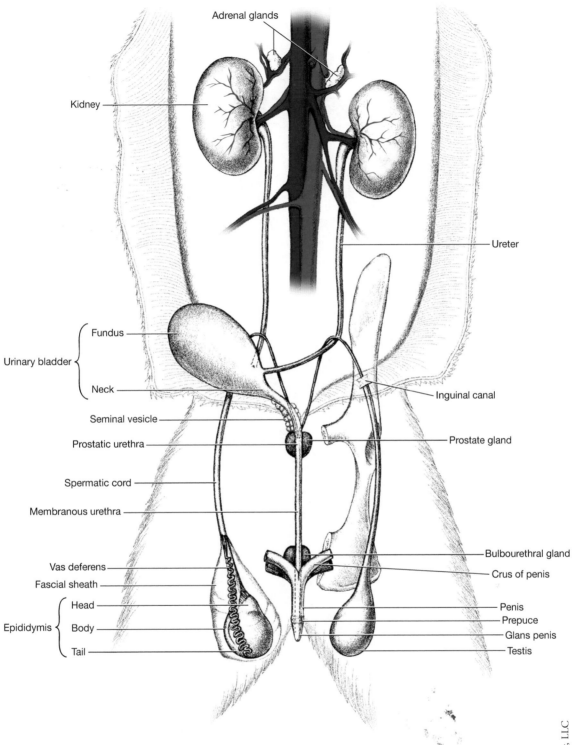

Adrenal glands

Kidney

Ureter

Fundus

Urinary bladder

Neck

Seminal vesicle

Prostatic urethra

Spermatic cord

Membranous urethra

Vas deferens

Fascial sheath

Epididymis { Head Body Tail

Inguinal canal

Prostate gland

Bulbourethral gland

Crus of penis

Penis

Prepuce

Glans penis

Testis

Figure 7.2 – Urogenital system of the male cat.

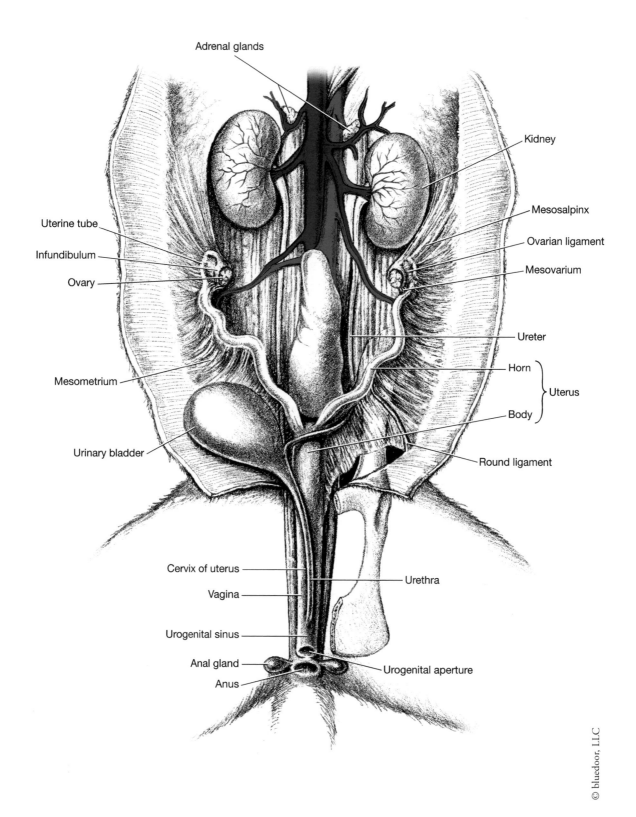

Adrenal glands

Kidney

Uterine tube

Mesosalpinx

Infundibulum

Ovarian ligament

Ovary

Mesovarium

Ureter

Horn

Mesometrium

Uterus

Body

Urinary bladder

Round ligament

Cervix of uterus

Urethra

Vagina

Urogenital sinus

Anal gland

Urogenital aperture

Anus

© bluedoor, LLC

Figure 7.3 – Urogenital system of the female cat.

nary bladder (Figures 7.2 and 7.3). The urinary bladder is a reservoir for urine. In the preserved state, it is empty and reduced in size, but when it fills with urine, it expands about 5-fold. The expanded cranial portion is the **fundus,** and the narrow caudal portion is the **neck.** Section the bladder along the frontal plane and note the wrinkled texture of the internal surface. These "wrinkles" are called **rugae.** Also note the points of entry of the two ureters at the dorsal wall and the exit opening to the urethra. These three openings form an internal triangle known as the **trigone.** The bladder is held in position ventrally by a median ligament and on each side by lateral ligaments, and is protected by pads of fat.

Urethra

The urethra is the duct that transports urine from the urinary bladder to the exterior of the body. Because the urethra lies mainly in the pelvic canal, you will observe it during dissection of the reproductive system (Figures 7.2 and 7.3). The urethra exhibits sexual dimorphism because its length varies between males and females. In the female, it is a short duct that empties to the exterior by way of the **urogenital orifice.** The caudal portion of the female urethra is also the caudal portion of the vagina, and is called the **vaginal vestibule** (or **urogenital sinus**). The male urethra is much longer, extending from the urinary bladder to the tip of the penis, where it opens as the **urogenital orifice.** The male urethra is associated with both urinary and reproductive functions, since it transports urine and semen. It is divided into three portions: the proximal portion is the **prostatic urethra,** the middle portion is the **membranous urethra,** and the distal portion extending through the penis is the **spongy urethra.** *The human urethra is very similar, except it opens to the exterior as the urinary meatus.*

THE REPRODUCTIVE SYSTEM

Your study of the reproductive system is divided into the male and female systems. On the basis of the descriptions that follow, determine the sex of your specimen, if you have not yet done so, and follow the appropriate dissection protocol. Then locate a specimen of the opposite sex within your lab, and examine it also.

Male Reproductive Structures

The organs of the male reproductive system include the male gonads, known as the testes, which are located within the scrotum. They also include the penis, a series of tubes that carry spermatozoa and fluids collectively called semen, and the glands that produce the fluid. The tubes include the epididymus, vas deferens, and urethra, and the glands are the seminal vesicles, prostate gland, and bulbourethral gland. Locate the following components of the male reproductive system in your male specimen (Figure 7.2).

Scrotum

The scrotum lies hidden beneath the fur of the region caudal to the penis and ventral to the pelvis. It is an integumentary sac that hangs below the pelvic wall and contains the male **gonads** (sex organs), the **testes.** Carefully make a cut through the dorsal wall of one side of the scrotum and, using scissors, cut the skin to the ventral margin. Repeat this cut on the opposite side. Now, peel the skin away to expose the two testes. Note the median septum that divides the scrotum internally in half, providing a separate chamber for each testis, known as the **cremasteric pouch.** Notice that the pouch narrows into a tubular structure at its ventral end. This structure is the **spermatic cord,** which contains the vas deferens, the spermatic artery and vein, and nerves.

Testes

The paired testes are the organs that produce the male **gametes,** or sex cells, and the male sex hormone, **testosterone.** Their outer coat, called the **tunica albuginea,** gives the testes a white, marbled appearance. With a sharp scalpel, cut one testis in half and notice the coiled tubules within. These are the **seminiferous tubules** and are the site where the male gametes, called **spermatozoa,** are produced.

Epididymus

On the dorsal part of each testis is an arrangement of tightly coiled tubules known as the **epididymus**. Locate the epididymus of your cat on the unsectioned testis. It is a comma-shaped organ that curves around the dorsal margin of the testis. From ventral to dorsal, it is divided into a **head**, a **body**, and a **tail**. The coiled tubule that forms the main part of the epididymus is called the **ductus epididymus**, which extends from the head region to the tail region, where it continues as the **vas deferens**.

Vas Deferens

The **vas deferens**, which may also be called the **ductus deferens**, extends from the epididymus to the urethra. From each testis, it begins as a coiled tube at its union with the ductus epididymus and continues in a cranial direction into the ventral body wall along with the spermatic artery, vein, and nerves as the **spermatic cord**. Follow the vas deferens to its point of entry into the body wall. Note that it passes through an opening called the **inguinal canal**. Once within the body cavity, it passes ventrally toward the ureter and turns medially until it reaches the dorsal wall of the urinary bladder. Do not attempt to trace the vas deferens further at this point in the dissection; you will need to open the pelvic cavity, which will be done soon. At the base of the bladder is a membranous, elongate sac called the **seminal vesicle**, which empties its secretions into the vas deferens via a small duct. Near the neck of the bladder, the vas deferens passes with its counterpart from the opposite side to the **prostate gland**, which is a glandular thickening of the dorsal wall of the seminal vesicle. The seminal vesicle and the prostate contribute fluids to form the semen. The vas deferens then passes through the prostatic tissue to unite with the urethra near its origin from the bladder.

Urethra

To observe the urethra and the male glands that contribute to semen, it is necessary to cut through the symphysis pubis. To do this, carefully make a 2.5-cm-long (1-inch) incision through the abdominal wall along the margin of the pelvis. With your fingers, find a slight depression in the midline between the pubic bones and with a sharp scalpel, cut into the depression and adjacent muscles. Plunge the scalpel deeply as you cut. Now separate the pelvic bones by grasping the hind limbs and push them laterally, completing the separation of the pelvis. Clean up the area by removing connective tissue and fat. With good technique, you should now be observing the organs of the pelvic wall, including the seminal vesicles at the base of the bladder and the whitish prostate gland immediately ventral to it. The tube extending from the urinary bladder to the prostate gland, emerging to extend through the penis, is the urethra. As described previously, it consists of a **prostatic urethra**, a **membranous urethra**, and a **spongy urethra**. The prostatic urethra is the proximal portion, extending from the urinary bladder through the prostate gland. The membranous urethra and spongy urethra are also known as the urogenital urethra. The membranous urethra extends a short distance to the base of the penis. It receives secretions from a small gland known as the **bulbourethral gland**, which contributes to semen. The spongy urethra extends through the penis. It opens to the exterior at the **urogenital orifice**, *which is called the urinary meatus in humans.*

Penis

The penis of the cat is obscured by a sheath of skin, which surrounds it. To observe the penis, grasp the opening of the sheath with a pair of forceps and make a cut through its ventral wall with scissors. Continue this cut along the ventral wall of the sheath, cutting through connective tissue to expose the penis completely. Of course, be careful to avoid cutting the penis at this point. The penis encloses the spongy urethra, which lies outside the pelvic canal. The free end of the penis, called the **glans penis**, lies within a pocket of skin called the **prepuce**. Cut open the prepuce to reveal completely the glans and the opening of the spongy urethra. Then cut through the penis along the longitudinal plane. Notice the columns of erectile tissue, which contain blood sinuses that fill with blood to produce erection. The columns are called **corpora cavernosa**. Their proximal ends are attached to the ischia by tough bands of connective tissue, known as **crura** (crus in the singular form). *The human penis is not contained within a sheath as in the cat, but hangs freely from its attachments to the pubic symphysis by way of the crura.*

The reproductive system of the cat includes **anal glands**, which are located near the anus. In male cats, contraction of the glands and nearby muscles causes fluid to spray outward, marking the cat's territory.

Female Reproductive Structures

The female gonads are the ovaries. Other female organs include the uterine tubes, uterus, vagina, and vulva. Locate and identify the following components of the female reproductive system in a female cat (Figure 7.3):

Ovaries

The ovaries are paired, oval organs that lie slightly caudolateral to the kidneys in the abdominopelvic cavity. They are anchored to the ventral body wall by the **suspensory ovarian ligament** and to the dorsal body wall by the larger **ovarian ligament**. The ovarian ligament connects each ovary to the cranial end of the uterus. A third ligament, the **mesovarium**, provides an additional connection between each ovary and the corresponding uterine horn. As the female gonads, the ovaries produce the female gametes, the **ova**, and the female sex hormones, estrogen and progesterone. During ovulation, or release of an ovum from an ovary, the ovum bursts through the ovarian wall to enter the abdominal cavity. Ideally, the ovum is then swept into the nearby opening to the uterine tube by ciliary currents.

Uterine tubes

Also known as oviducts, or fallopian tubes, the paired uterine tubes transport ova that have been released during ovulation from the ovaries. If fertilization is to occur, it usually occurs within the upper one-third of a uterine tube. The fertilized ovum, called a zygote, is then transported by ciliary currents within the tube to the uterus for implantation. Carefully reflect the ovary and uterine tubes to the side, and notice that the cranial extremity of each uterine tube curves laterally over each ovary to form a hood-like expansion

called the **infundibulum** and opens medially by way of the **ostium tubae**. The outer margins of the infundibulum contain finger-like projections, called **fimbriae**. Each uterine tube is attached to the dorsal body wall by a broad ligament known as the **mesosalpinx**. The distal end of each uterine tube merges with a uterine horn, which is larger in diameter. *The uterine tubes of the human female are comparatively much greater in length, extending from the infundibulum surrounding an ovary to the pelvic cavity to unite with the uterus.*

Uterus

The uterus of the cat includes two **uterine horns**, right and left, that begin as continuations of the uterine tubes. They descend into the pelvic cavity, where they unite to form the **body** of the uterus. The combination of the uterine horns and body form the Y-shaped uterus. The mesentery supporting the uterus is known as the **mesometrium**, and an additional structure, called the **round ligament**, adds strength to the mesometrium as it extends diagonally across it. The distal end of the uterus is slightly tapered, forming the **cervix**, which unites with the vagina. *The uterus of the human female is not Y-shaped, but resembles the shape of a pear, instead. It receives the right and left uterine tubes at its superior border, which is a rounded area known as the fundus. The constricted part of the uterus is known as the cervix, and its internal channel is the cervical canal. Also, the junction of the uterus and vagina is a distinct separation between the two organs.*

Vagina

To view the vagina and other caudal parts of the reproductive system, you will need to expose the pelvic cavity. Begin by making a 2.5-cm-long (1-inch) incision horizontally along the pelvic rim, cutting through muscles and fat. Insert a finger to find the symphysis pubis, which will feel like a shallow groove near the midventral line. Once you've located it, cut through it with a pair of scissors or bone cutters, but be careful to avoid plunging the instrument too deeply. You will be cutting through deep muscles and the cartilage of the symphysis pubis, if you are cutting correctly.

After cutting, grasp the hindlimbs and separate the pelvic bones to expose the pelvic wall. Carefully clean away connective tissue and fat, and find the body of the uterus once again. Trace it to its narrowed distal part, the cervix, which protrudes into the vagina. The vagina extends from its origin near the cervix to its opening to the **urogenital sinus** at the **vaginal orifice**. Because the urogenital sinus also receives the opening of the urethra, the **urethral orifice**, it is a common channel for the urinary and reproductive fluids.

Vulva

The vulva is the female external structure that includes the urogenital aperture, labia, and clitoris. The **urogenital aperture** is the exterior opening from the urogenital sinus, which is common to the urinary and reproductive systems. Bordering the urogenital aperture on both sides are the small **labia**, which are very small in the cat and, therefore, difficult to observe. However, you should be able to identify the **clitoris**, represented as a small projection at the cranial union of the labia. It rests in a shallow, midventral depression. The clitoris is the homologous structure to the penis, although in most mammals, the urethra does not pass through it. Similar to the male, **anal glands** are present on either side of the anus. *The human vulva contains two pairs of labia, majora and minora, rather than a single pair, as seen in the cat. Also, the human clitoris is a more prominent structure. Finally, the urethra and vagina enter the vulva as separate openings in human females: as the urethral orifice and the vaginal orifice.*

CHAPTER REVIEW

A. Answer the following multiple-choice questions by circling the most correct answer.

1. The urogenital organs that function in the formation of urine are the
   a. urethra
   b. kidneys
   c. spleen and thymus
   d. ureters and urinary bladder

2. Organs that have a different structure between males and females are
   a. called sexually dimorphic
   b. the ureters
   c. the kidneys
   d. the urinary bladder

3. The blood becomes filtered, water is reabsorbed, and excess ions are secreted within
   a. the gonads
   b. nephrons
   c. the renal pelvis
   d. ureters

4. Renal pyramids may be found within the
   a. renal capsule
   b. renal medulla
   c. renal cortex
   d. renal pelvis

5. From the ureters, urine flows into the
   a. urinary bladder
   b. renal pelvis
   c. urethra
   d. kidneys

6. In the female cat, the urethra opens to the exterior as the
   a. vagina
   b. urogenital orifice
   c. urinary meatus
   d. urethral orifice

7. The dorsal part of each testis is an arrangement of tightly coiled tubules known as the
   a. vas deferens
   b. seminal vesicles
   c. epididymus
   d. spermatic cord

8. Near the neck of the bladder, the vas deferens passes with its counterpart from the opposite side to the
   a. epididymis
   b. prostate gland
   c. seminal vesicles
   d. ureter

9. As the female gonads, the _____ produce the female gametes called ova.
   a. testes
   b. uterus
   c. ovaries
   d. fallopian tubes

10. The distal end of the uterus is slightly tapered, forming the_____, which unites with the vagina.
    a. vas deferens
    b. cervix
    c. uterine cavity
    d. vestibule

B. Complete the sentences below by providing the missing terms from the chapter material.

1. Urine formation occurs in the kidneys, at the site of functional subunits called _____.

2. The _____ _____ is a membrane-lined basin in the center of each kidney, which unites with the mucous membrane lining the ureter.

3. The three openings into the urinary bladder form an internal triangle known as the _____.

4. The _____ is the duct that transports urine from the urinary bladder to the exterior of the body.

5. The integumentary sac that hangs below the pelvic wall and contains the testes is called the _____.

6. The coiled tubules within the testes, where spermatozoa are produced, are called _____ _____.

7. The ductus epididymus continues as a tube of larger diameter known as the _____ _____.

8. Each ovary is supported to the dorsal body wall by the _____ _____.

9. The uterus of the cat includes two _____ _____, right and left, that begin as continuations of the uterine tubes.

10. The _____ _____ is the exterior opening from the urogenital sinus in the female cat, which is common to the urinary and reproductive systems.

C. Answer the following descriptive and critical-thinking questions with a brief explanation in the spaces provided.

1. Describe the functional importance of nephrons and where they are located. _____

    _____

    _____

    _____

    _____

    _____

2. Trace the pathway of spermatozoa during an ejaculation. _____

_____

_____

_____

_____

_____

3. Compare and contrast the vulva of a cat and a human. _____

_____

_____

_____

_____

_____

_____

c h a p t e r   e i g h t

THE NERVOUS SYSTEM AND SPECIAL SENSES

The nervous system provides a system of communication between its primary organ, the **brain**, and the distant parts of the body. Its goal is to monitor changes in the environment inside and outside the body, interpret the changes, and initiate a response in an effort to maintain homeostasis. It does all of this by way of electrochemical messages called **nerve impulses**. Nerve impulses race through the body every moment, traveling along special routes, or **nerves**, at high speeds.

As a whole, the nervous system is a complex series of organs and structures that extend throughout the body. In addition to the brain, its organs include the spinal cord, nerves, ganglia, and sensory receptors. The nervous system is divided into two main categories: the **central nervous system (CNS)**, which includes the brain and spinal cord, and the **peripheral nervous system (PNS)**, which includes the nerves, ganglia, and sensory receptors. The PNS is further divided in an **afferent** (sensory) **system**, which carries impulses from receptors to the CNS, and an **efferent** (motor) **system**, which carries impulses from the CNS to effectors, such as muscles and glands. The efferent system is itself divided into a **somatic system**, in which impulses are carried to skeletal muscles, and an **autonomic system**, which carries impulses to glands and smooth muscles. Finally, the autonomic system is divided into a **sympathetic division** and a **parasympathetic division**.

This chapter enables you to explore the structures of the nervous system of the cat. You will remove the brain from the cranial cavity to examine it, observe the spinal cord, and trace the major nerves throughout the body. You will also examine the **special sensory organs**, which are associated with the nervous system. They include the eyes, ears, taste organs of the tongue, and smelling centers in the nasal epithelium.

CENTRAL NERVOUS SYSTEM

The central nervous system, which includes the brain and spinal cord, represents the center of nervous system structure and function. You will study the brain of the cat first, which requires removal of the brain from the cranial cavity. In some labs, the cat brain may be substituted for a sheep brain. Because both are typical of a mammalian brain, either is suitable for this study.

To remove the brain from the cranium of your cat, follow the protocol outlined below. As you progress through this procedure, identify the three membrane layers that surround the brain and spinal cord. Collectively known as the

meninges, they are the outer **dura mater**, the middle **arachnoid**, and the innermost **pia mater**.

1. Clean the dorsal skull and neck regions completely of skin, muscle, and connective tissue.

2. Using a pair of sharp bone shears, cut the 3rd, 2nd, and 1st cervical vertebrae, and remove the bone fragments with forceps. Sever the spinal cord with a clean cut as far caudally as possible.

3. Very carefully insert the pointed half of your bone shears slightly through the

foramen magnum at the base of the skull, but don't go too deep! Close the shears and apply pressure. This should crack the thick occipital bone.

4. From the cracked occipital bone, cut around the skullcap above the eye orbits with bone shears, but again be very careful to avoid cutting too deeply. Once you've cut a complete circle, carefully lift the skullcap off. Note the tough dura mater that covers the brain. The outermost of the meninges, it is composed of tough, fibrous connective tissue. In some areas, it is connected to the inner surface of the skull, and, thus, may have been damaged as you cut through the cranium. Carefully pull the dura mater away from the brain to expose the underlying meningeal layers, and make a cut through it with a scalpel from rostral to caudal. As you do so, note the extension of the dura mater between the two cerebral hemispheres, which is called the **falx cerebri**, and the extension between the cerebrum and the cerebellum, known as the **tentorium**. These membranes help anchor the brain within the cranial cavity.

5. Using a pair of forceps, carefully remove the remaining pieces of bone. In the caudal section of the cranial cavity, cut out and remove the small bone segments protecting the delicate cerebellum. Continue to remove bone pieces until the brain is well exposed. With the dura mater removed, note the meningeal layer beneath it, known as the **arachnoid**. It is composed of loose connective tissue arranged in a cobweb-like arrangement. The arachnoid passes over the shallow grooves, or **sulci**, of the brain's surface. The upfolds of the brain are called **gyri**. With your forceps, pick away the thin membrane adhering to the surface of the brain. This is the deepest meningeal layer, the **pia mater**. The pia mater is

separated from the arachnoid by a fluid-filled space called the **subarachnoid space**, which is continuous around the brain and spinal cord. A slightly yellowish fluid circulates within this space to provide a liquid cushion for the CNS, and is known as **cerebrospinal fluid (CSF)**.

6. To remove the brain from the cranial cavity, begin by lifting the severed spinal cord from the floor of the vertebral canal. Then lift the brain from the floor of the cranial cavity by working caudally and very cautiously. As you do so, sever the cranial nerves from the brain with a sharp scalpel (this is a good job for a partner if one is available). Make your cuts as far from the brain as possible to facilitate their identification later.

Brain

The mammalian brain contains three primary divisions: the forebrain, the midbrain, and the hindbrain. Before identifying the structures of the brain, many of which require sectioning of the brain in half to observe, turn the brain on its dorsal side to expose the ventral surface. Using Table 8.1 as a reference, identify the **cranial nerves**, whose cut ends should be visible as shown in Figure 8.1. Following this exercise, observe the parts of the brain as described.

FOREBRAIN (prosencephalon): the largest division of the brain. Occupying the cranial and middle regions, it consists of the large telencephalon and the much smaller diencephalon (Figures 8.1 - 8.3).
Telencephalon: consists of the largest single structure of the brain, the **cerebrum**. The cerebrum is convoluted in the cat, although much more so in the human. Note the downfolds, or **sulci**, and the upfolds, or **gyri**. The cerebrum consists of two halves, the right and left **cerebral hemispheres**, which are separated by a deep furrow called the **longitudinal fissure**. Separate the

Cranial Nerve	Union with Brain	Innervations	Sensation or Action
Olfactory (I)	olfactory lobe	sensory endings in nasal epithelium	sense of olfaction (smell)
Optic (II)	rostral colliculi and thalamus	sensory cells in the retina of each eye	sense of vsion (sight)
Oculomotor (III)	cerebral peduncles of midbrain	intrinsic and extrinsic eye muscles	movement of eye, control of light entering eye
Trochlear (IV)	roof of midbrain	superior oblique muscle of eye	movement of eye

Trigeminal (V):
  1. Ophthalmic
 	
  2. Maxillary
 	
  3. Mandibular
	lateral portions of pons	external eyeball, skin of skull
		
		vibrissae and upper teeth
		
		jaw, skin of lower face, teeth of lower jaw, mouth, tongue
			sensations of face region
			
			sensations of rostrum
			
			movement of jaw; sensations of lower face and mouth

Abducens (VI)	rostral end of medulla	rectus externus muscle of eye	movement of eye
Facial (VII)	medulla caudal to CN VI	jaw and face muscles	mastication and facial expression
Auditory (VIII)	lateral medulla	sensory cells within cochlea of inner ear	sense of audation (hearing)
Glossopharyngeal (IX)	lateral medulla	pharynx, parotid gland, caudal portion of tongue	sense of gustation (taste), sensations of throat region
Vagus (X)	lateral medulla	muscles of the pharynx, larynx, thoracic viscera, abdominal visceral; sensory of larynx, and thoracic and abdominal viscera	contraction of innervated muscles; sensation of innervated regions
Spinal accessory (XI)	lateral medulla	muscles of the neck and pharyngeal region	movement of the neck and pharynx
Hypoglossal (XII)	ventral medulla	tongue and hyoid muscles	movement of the tongue

Table 8.1 – The cranial nerves.

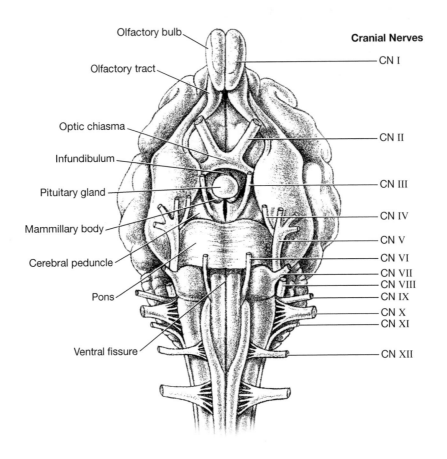

Olfactory bulb
Olfactory tract
Optic chiasma
Infundibulum
Pituitary gland
Mammillary body
Cerebral peduncle
Pons
Ventral fissure

Cranial Nerves
CN I
CN II
CN III
CN IV
CN V
CN VI
CN VII
CN VIII
CN IX
CN X
CN XI
CN XII

© bluedoor, LLC

Figure 8.1 – Cranial nerves (ventral aspect of the brain).

hemispheres by spreading them apart with your fingers, and you will see a thick, transverese band of white matter that connects the hemispheres. This bridge is the **corpus callosum**. Now make a midsagittal section through the brain by cutting deeply through the longitudinal fissure. Use a long, sharp knife for this procedure to make a single, clean cut through the brain. The corpus callosum includes an expanded rostral end, called the **genu**, a thinner middle section known as the **trunk**, and an expanded caudal end known as the **splenium**. The ventral continuation of the splenium is called the **fornix**. Immediately inferior to the corpus callosum is a cavity, called the **lateral ventricle**, which is one of four ventricles in the brain (two lateral ventri-

cles, one **third ventricle**, and one **fourth ventricle**; you will identify the third and fourth ventricles a bit later). They contain clusters of capillaries and ventricular cells. The cell clusters are known as **choroid plexi**, which serve as the source of cerebrospinal fluid (CSF). The **septum pellucidim** may be visible, which is a thin membrane separating the two lateral ventricles. At the rostral end of the cerebrum is located a pair of swellings, called the **olfactory lobes**. They represent the terminal points of olfactory nerves originating from the nasal epithelium. The Olfactory Nerves (CN I) extend from the olfactory lobes to the cerebrum. A second deep furrow, called the **transverse fissure**, separates the cerebrum from the smaller cerebellum located on the caudal side of the brain. The cerebrum is the integrative center of the brain. It receives sensory information, processes it with memory connections, and initiates motor responses. Its primary functional zone is the outer fringe of gray matter, known as the **cerebral cortex**. White matter is found deep to the cortex, which serves as communication pathways. Embedded within the white matter of both hemispheres are islands of gray matter called the **basal ganglia**.

Diencephalon: the region of the brain located ventral to the cerebrum and immediately below the lateral ventricles. Its most prominent structure is the bilobed **thalamus**, which forms the central portion and lateral walls of the diencepahlon. The thalamus is a switchboard for impulses traveling to and from the cerebrum. At its ventral border is the much smaller **hypothalamus**, which serves as a cen-

ter for autonomic functions and triggers the **pituitary gland** (hypophysis) that is attached to it via a narrow stalk. A second endocrine gland, the **pineal gland,** is the small, round structure that projects from the roof of the diencephalon. Ventral to the pineal gland is the **third ventricle**. It receives CSF from the two lateral ventricles via a small channel called the **foramen of Monro**. Turn the brain over to expose the ventral surface, and find the X-shaped **optic chiasma**. It is the crossing of the two Optic Nerves (CN II).

MIDBRAIN (mesencephalon): a small part of the brain, which is located ventral to the forebrain (Figure 8.3). Its major portions are the tectum and the cerebral peduncles.

Tectum: forms the roof of the midbrain, and can be observed as the swellings in the center of the brain rostral to the cerebellum. The swellings are the **corpora quadrigemina**. The larger rostral

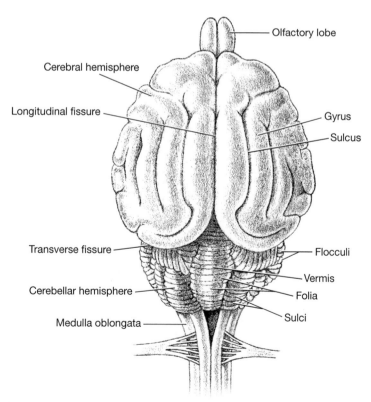

Figure 8.2 – Brain (dorsal aspect).

Olfactory lobe

Cerebral hemisphere

Longitudinal fissure

Gyrus

Sulcus

Transverse fissure

Flocculi

Vermis

Cerebellar hemisphere

Folia

Medulla oblongata

Sulci

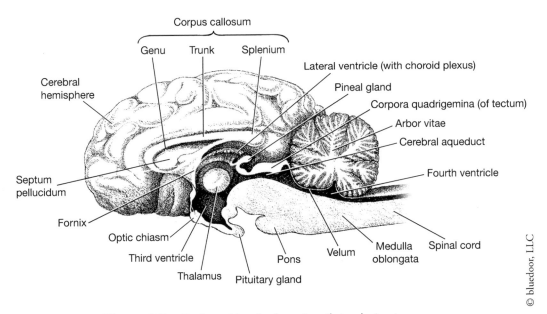

Figure 8.3 – Brain, midsagittal section (lateral view).

pair is called the **rostral colliculi**, and the smaller caudal pair is the **caudal colliculi**.

Cerebral peduncles: a pair of fiber bundles that form the ventrolateral surface of the midbrain.

HINDBRAIN (rhombencephalon): the caudal part of the brain, it consists of the metencephalon and the myelencephalon (Figures 8.2 - 8.3).

Metencephalon: the cranial part of the hindbrain. The **cerebellum** dominates most of the metencephalon, forming the dorsal component. Its surface area is increased by numerous folds, known as **folia**, which are separated from each other by shallow grooves, or **sulci**. The central portion of the cerebellum, the **vermis**, is composed by white matter, as you can observe in the sectioned brain. Numerous branches of gray matter extend from it to the outer surface. This branching arrangement is called the **arbor vitae** (tree of life). Lateral to the vermis are the right and left **cerebellar hemispheres** and their lateral extensions,

the **flocculi**. The outer surface, which is composed of gray matter, is called the **cerebellar cortex**. The ventral component of the metencephalon is formed by a rounded swelling at the cranial end of the brain stem, called the **pons varolii**. The pons is connected to the cerebellum by transverse fibers.

Myelencephalon: the caudal part of the midbrain, which is also the caudal extremity of the brain. The myelencephalon includes the **medulla oblongata**, which is the transitional region between the brain and the spinal cord. Together with the pons varolii and midbrain, the three brain structures form the **brain stem**. The **fourth ventricle** is located between the cerebellum and the medulla. It receives CSF by way of the narrow **cerebral aqueduct** (aqueduct of Sylvius), which runs through the midbrain.

Spinal Cord

The spinal cord is a semicyclindrical mass of gray and white matter enveloped by the meninges

(Figure 8.4). Beginning at its cranial end as a caudal continuation of the medulla oblongata, it passes through the vertebral canal and tapers at the 7th lumbar segment to a bundle of nerves called the **cauda equina**. The spinal cord terminates as a slender filament, the **filum terminale**, in the base of the tail. In the cervical and lumbosacral regions, the spinal cord contains swellings that give rise to the nerves that innervate the front and hind limbs, respectively.

A pair of **spinal nerves** arise from each segment and exit the vertebral column via intervertebral foramina. The spinal nerves are named according to the region of the vertebral column where they arise. A spinal nerve is formed by the union of a **ventral root** and a **dorsal root**. After exiting the vertebral column, the spinal nerve divides into a **dorsal ramus**, which supplies the muscles of the back, and a thicker **ventral ramus**, which supplies the remaining somatic muscles of the body.

You should not attempt to remove the entire spinal cord of your cat at this time, because of the damage this dissection would cause to spinal and peripheral nerves. Instead, obtain a cross section of the cord by cutting off the caudal tip of the region below the brain stem of the brain. Using this section, locate the following components of the spinal cord (Figure 8.5):

MENINGES: continuous with the meninges of the brain, the three membranes are the outermost **dura mater**, which continues to the 2nd sacral vertebral segment where it fuses with the pia mater; the **middle arachnoid**; and the deep **pia mater**, which adheres to the surface of the spinal cord. Similar to the brain meninges, the arachnoid and pia mater are separated by the **subarachnoid space**, in which CSF circulates.

SPINAL CORD GRAY MATTER: the H-shaped mass of nerve tissue at the center of the spinal cord. The gray matter of the cord consists of the **gray commissure**, which is the central bridge connecting the left and right sides of the H; the **anterior** (ventral) **gray horns**, located on the ventral side of the spinal cord and which form the larger of the two horn segments of the H; the **posterior** (dorsal) **gray horns**, located on the dorsal side of the spinal cord; and the **lateral gray horns**, located between the anterior and posterior gray horns. Note also the small hole in the center of the gray commissure. This is the **central canal**, which runs the entire length of the cord and carries CSF.

SPINAL CORD WHITE MATTER: the white nerve tissue surrounding the gray matter horns. The white matter consists of ascending tracts of sensory fibers and descending tracts of motor nerve fibers.

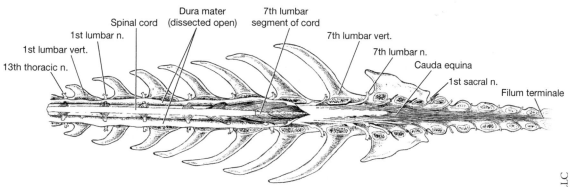

13th thoracic n. | 1st lumbar vert. | 1st lumbar n. | Spinal cord | Dura mater (dissected open) | 7th lumbar segment of cord | 7th lumbar vert. | 7th lumbar n. | Cauda equina | 1st sacral n. | Filum terminale

Figure 8.4 – Spinal cord (dorsal view of dissected cord within vertebral column).

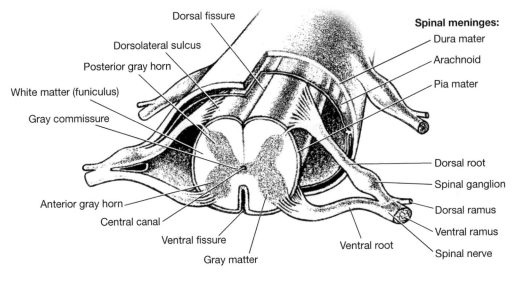

Dorsal fissure

Dorsolateral sulcus

Posterior gray horn

White matter (funiculus)

Gray commissure

Spinal meninges:
Dura mater
Arachnoid
Pia mater

Dorsal root
Spinal ganglion
Dorsal ramus
Ventral ramus
Spinal nerve

Anterior gray horn

Central canal

Ventral fissure

Ventral root

Gray matter

© bluedoor, LLC

Figure 8.5 – Spinal cord (cross section).

PERIPHERAL NERVOUS SYSTEM

The peripheral nervous system (PNS) consists of the **motor** (efferent) **nerves** that carry impulses from the CNS to PNS effectors, and the **sensory** (afferent) **nerves** that carry impulses in the opposite direction. The following study of the PNS includes the somatic division of the PNS, which contains the networks of nerves arising from the ventral rami that innervate skeletal muscles and a brief description of the autonomic division of the PNS.

Somatic Division

The somatic division of the PNS includes branching networks of nerves known as plexi, and the various peripheral nerves extending from the plexi to skeletal muscles. In the musculature of your cat, locate the following plexi and major peripheral nerves (Figure 8.6):

CERVICAL PLEXUS: the least extensive of the three major plexi, it is formed by the ventral rami of the cervical region. The nerves associated with the cervical plexus supply the musculature and skin of the neck region. It can be located by tracing the ventral rami of the

neck from the dorsal side as they emerge from the vertebral column.

BRACHIAL PLEXUS: located medial to the shoulder and cranial to the 1st rib, it can be observed from the ventral side deep to the pectoral muscles. The brachial plexus is formed by the union of the ventral rami of the 5th to 8th cervical and 1st thoracic nerves. From the brachial plexus arise the following nerves:

Pectoral nerves: several small nerves that arise from the ventral divisions of the plexus.

Scapular nerves: two nerves, a scapular and a suprascapular nerve, both of which arise mostly from the 6th cervical root.

Axillary nerve: a large nerve located caudal to the scapular nerves. It passes through the brachium ventral to the long head of the triceps.

Subscapular nerve: two small nerves that arise from the plexus near the origin of the axillary and continue dorsal to it.

Radial nerve: a large, deep nerve located caudal to the axillary. It is formed by

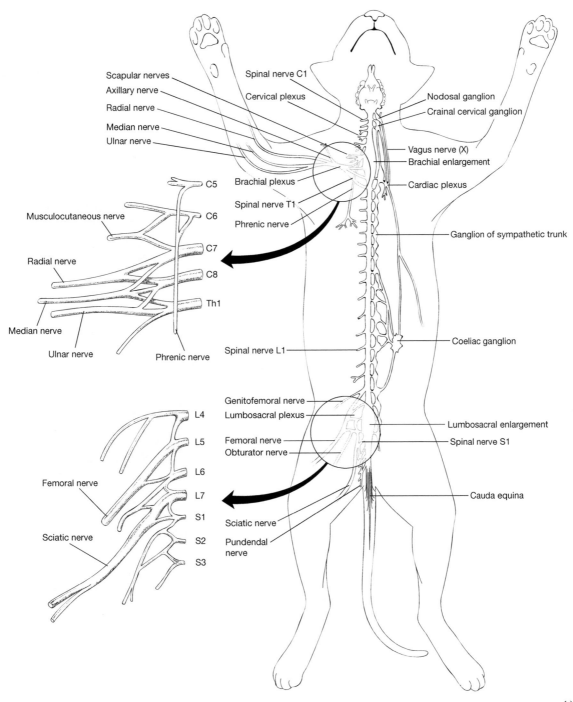

Figure 8.6 – Nervous system of the cat.

the union of the 7th and 8th cervical and 1st thoracic nerves.

Musculocutaneous nerve: arising from the 6th and 7th cervical nerves, it passes superficial to the radial nerve into the brachium.

Median nerve: a prominent nerve that runs down the medial side of the brachium. It is a ventral division of the 7th and 8th cervical and 1st thoracic nerves.

Ulnar nerve: arising caudal to the median nerve, the ulnar is similar to the median nerve in its pathway.

LUMBOSACRAL PLEXUS: formed by the ventral rami of seven spinal nerves (4th lumbar to 3rd sacral), it supplies the skin and muscles of the pelvis and hind limbs. Because it lies deep within the abdominal and pelvic cavities, you will not observe it in your specimen. However, identify the following peripheral nerves that originate from this plexus in the hip and thigh musculature of your cat.

Genitofemoral nerve: a division of the 4th lumbar nerve, it passes caudally through the pelvic wall.

Femoral nerve: a large nerve that arises primarily from the 5th and 6th lumbar nerves. It passes through the pelvic wall on the ventral side along with the femoral artery and vein.

Obturator nerve: arising from the unification of a second division of the 6th lumbar nerve and a second division of the 5th lumbar nerve, it extends caudolaterally through the obturator internus muscle and the obturator foramen.

Sciatic nerve: a continuation of the **lumbosacral trunk**, which receives the 6th and 7th lumbar nerves and the 1st and 2nd sacral nerves. The sciatic nerve continues down the lateral side of the thigh to divide into the **tibial** and **fibular** (common peroneal) **nerves.**

Autonomic Division

The autonomic division of the PNS innervates smooth muscles and glands. Its major components include the following ganglia, rami, and nerves, some of which are diagrammed in Figure 8.6. Autonomic components are divided into two distinct groups: the **sympathetic division**, which carries impulses that activate body responses to emergency situations, and the **parasympathetic division**, which carries impulses that dominate when the body is at rest.

SYMPATHETIC TRUNK GANGLIA: a vertical row of ganglia, which are clusters of neuron cell bodies, extending along both sides of the vertebral column from the base of the skull to the tail. These ganglia receive sympathetic fibers originating from the spinal cord. Collectively, the sympathetic trunk ganglia are referred to as the **sympathetic chain.**

PREVERTEBRAL GANGLIA: also known as collateral ganglia, they are located ventral to the vertebral column and close to large abdominal arteries. Prevertebral ganglia receive sympathetic fibers originating from the spinal cord.

TERMINAL GANGLIA: also known as intramural ganglia, they are located at the end of visceral efferent pathways near or on the walls of visceral effectors, such as smooth muscle and glands. The terminal ganglia receive parasympathetic fibers that originate from the spinal cord.

COMMUNICATING RAMI: spinal nerve branches that carry impulses to or from sympathetic trunk ganglia. In the thoracic and upper lumber segments, they contain myelinated fibers to form the **white communicating rami**, or nonmyelinated fibers to form the **gray communicating rami**. In the remaining vertebral segments all of the communicating rami are gray.

VAGUS NERVE (X): a large cranial nerve that was described previously. It contains sympathetic and parasympathetic fibers that supply major thoracic and abdominal visceral organs.

PHRENIC NERVE: a large nerve that arises from the ventral rami of the 5th and 6th cervical nerves and passes caudally through the thoracic cavity to innervate the diaphragm.

ORGANS OF SPECIAL SENSE

The special senses are specialized parts of the body that provide the brain with information about the outside environment. There are four special senses: olfaction (smell), gustation (taste), vision (sight), and audation (hearing). The four special senses are perceived with the help of highly specialized organs. They are sensory patches within the nasal epithelium (olfaction), taste organs on the tongue (gustation), the eyes (vision), and the ears (audation). In each case, the special sensory organ contains sensory receptors. The sensory receptors are sensitive to a particular stimulus, and generate a nerve impulse when the stimulus is sufficiently strong. The nerve impulse then travels to the brain for interpretation.

Olfaction

The sense organs responsible for smell reception may be found within a patch of the mucosa lining the nasal cavity. Located in the dorsocaudal part of each nasal chamber, it is called the **olfactory mucosa**. The receptors in the ofactory mucosa are olfactory hair cells. The hair cells include dendrites, which appear under the microscope like tiny hairs that project into the mucosal lining. When the hair cells make contact with dissolved chemicals in the mucosa, they generate a nerve impulse. The impulse passes to adjacent sensory neurons that form olfactory nerves, which extend to the olfactory lobe. At the olfactory lobe, the olfactory nerves synapse at sensory neurons, which transmit the impulse to the cerebral cortex for interpretation.

Gustation

The taste receptors are organized into specialized groups of cells, known as the **taste buds**. Most taste buds are located on the fungiform and circumvallate papillae of the tongue. Taste buds contain neurons with dendrites that project onto the surface of the papillae, and are sensitive to dissolved chemicals. From the front, or oral, part of the tongue, impulses generated by the sensory neurons in the taste buds are transmitted via a branch of the facial nerve (CN VII). From the back, or pharyngeal, part of the tongue, impulses are transmitted via the glossopharyngeal nerve (CN IX).

Vision

The eye lies within its protective bony orbit. During your earlier observation of the cat's surface anatomy, you identified the palpebrae (eyelids) and the nictitating membrane. At this time, identify also the **conjunctiva**, which is a thin transparent membrane covering the underside of each eyelid and the surface of the eyeball. Also, find the **harderian gland**, which is a small gland on the medial surface of the nictitating membrane. Now, free the eyeball from the orbit rim and push it forward to observe the **lacrimal gland**, which produces tears. Now push the eyeball dorsally until it can be extracted from the orbit completely, and sever the optic nerve. Some of the **extrinsic eye muscles** will also require cutting.

From Figure 8.7, identify the extrinsic eye muscles, which move the eyeball. There are seven muscles: four recti originate on the bone around the optic foramen and insert on the sclera (white exterior covering of the eyeball) just behind the midline, or equator, of the eyeball. They are known as the **superior, inferior, lateral,** and **medial recti** muscles according to their position. A **retractor** muscle also originates from the optic foramen, and inserts on the sclera around the entrance to the optic nerve. The two oblique muscles, the **superior oblique** and **inferior oblique**, are evident only if the lateral and dorsal walls of the orbit are removed.

With one eye from your cat removed, observe its external features. Then, using a sharp scalpel, cut it into two equal parts along the equatorial plane. Since the internal structures of the eye are difficult to observe in a cat, you may be asked to study a preserved or fresh cow eye instead, which is anatomically similar. The eye includes the

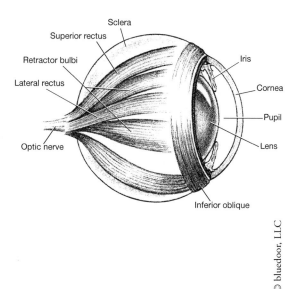

Sclera
Superior rectus
Retractor bulbi
Lateral rectus
Optic nerve
Inferior oblique
Iris
Cornea
Pupil
Lens

© bluedoor, LLC

Figure 8.7 – External eye with extrinsic muscles (lateral view).

following major structures, some of which are illustrated in Figure 8.7:

SCLERA: the white outer layer of the eyeball, which is composed of fibrous connective tissue. The sclera provides support for the eyeball.

CORNEA: a rostral continuation of the sclera that is transparent. The conjunctiva meets the cornea along its outer edge. The **anterior chamber** is located immediately behind the cornea.

IRIS: the pigmented ring of smooth muscle, which surrounds the black central hole. Involuntary impulses regulate contraction of the iris, which serves as a diaphragm to regulate the amount of light that enters the interior of the eye.

PUPIL: the black hole in the center of the iris, through which light enters the eye.

CHOROID: a vascular, black pigmented layer internal to the sclera. It helps to nourish the retina, and the pigments reduce the scattering of light rays to improve visual efficiency.

CILIARY BODY: a series of folds, forming a thickened ring within the eyeball between the choroid and iris junction.

LENS: the large oval or spherical structure that is suspended by **suspensory ligaments** extend-

ing from the ciliary body, located behind the pupil. Normally transparent, it is composed of dense protein formations. Immediately behind the lens is the **posterior chamber**, which contains a gelatinous **vitreous humor**.

RETINA: the innermost layer of the eyeball lining the posterior wall. It contains specialized sensory receptors, known as rod cells and cone cells, which generate a nerve impulse when they become activated by light. From the rods and cones, the nerve impulse is passed to two additional layers of neurons, the last of which converge at the **optic disc** to form the optic nerve (CN I). The optic nerve carries the impulse to the thalamus, and relays it to the occipital lobe of the cerebral cortex, where the impulses are interpreted into the sense of vision.

Audation

The ear contains the sense organs for both hearing and equilibrium. It consists of three parts: the external ear, the middle ear, and the internal ear.

EXTERNAL EAR: the part of the ear exposed to the external environment. It includes the following components:

Pinna: also known as the **auricle**, it is the external appendage on each side of the head of mammals. The pinna funnel mechanical vibrations (sound waves) into the head. Each consists of cartilage that is covered with skin, and is connected to extrinsic auricular muscles whose contraction moves the pinna in the direction of sound.

External auditory meatus: a skin-lined canal extending from the pinna to the tympanic membrane. It includes ceruminous glands, which secrete a waxy substance that lubricates the meatus and traps foreign particles.

Tympanic membrane: a thin membrane that separates the interior end of the external auditory meatus and the middle ear. It vibrates in response to sound waves, and transmits the vibration to the middle ear ossicles.

MIDDLE EAR: the cavity within the tympanic bulla of the skull, which is also known as the **tympanic cavity**. Dissection of the middle ear is extremely difficult, and is not recommended unless time and advanced dissection skills are available. If you wish to attempt it, you will remove the tympanic bulla from the cranium. To do this, first prepare the area by removing all soft tissues around the tympanic bulla. Using bone shears, cut through the bulla and medial (petrous) portion of the temporal bone from the skull. Next, remove the medial wall of the tympanic bulla by cutting with bone shears. Notice that the cavity within the bulla is separated into a larger lateral and a smaller medial chamber by a vertical wall of bone. Carefully break away this vertical plate of bone to expose the lateral chamber, which reveals the inner surface of the tympanic membrane and its attached middle ear ossicle (the malleus). Then, with your bone shears, fracture the thick bony connection between the caudal end of the petrous bone and the caudal part of the bony ring surrounding the external auditory meatus. Using Figure 8.8 as a guide, identify the following parts of the middle ear:

Malleus: the first and largest ossicle, it connects the inner surface of the tympanic membrane to the second ossicle.

Incus: the middle ossicle, which contacts the malleus to transmit vibrations from it to the third ossicle.

Stapes: the third ossicle, which articulates with the incus. Its distal end forms a flattened disc, which fits over an ocal opening in the lateral wall of the tympanic cavity called the **fenestra vestibuli** (oval window). A round opening, called the **fenestra cochlea** (round window), is located slightly below the oval window.

INNER EAR: a series of winding canals surrounded by bone within the mastoid portion of the temporal bone, it is also called the **labyrinth**. It consists of an outer series of canals within walls of bone, known as the **bony labyrinth**, and an inner series of canals lined with membrane, called the **membranous labyrinth**. In life, fluid is present in each canal. Because of its very small size, the inner ear is extremely difficult to dissect. But if you wish to attempt it, it can be done by carefully chipping away the temporal bone medial to the tympanic cavity. With patience applied, you will gradually find the bony labyrinth embedded within the bone of this region. Using Figure 8.8 as a guide, identify the following parts of the inner ear:

Cochlea: a coiled, snail-shell-like part of the labyrinth that contains hair cells, which are the sensory receptors for audation. The hair cells are sensory neurons with dendrites, which generate a nerve impulse when the fluid surrounding them moves in response to mechanical vibrations.

Semicircular canals: three loops of bony labyrinth that contain sensory receptors, which are activated by body movement. They transmit nerve impulses to the brain for the interpretation of equilibrium. The receptors are located within expanded areas at the base of the loops known as **ampullae**.

Vestibule: a small chamber between the cochlea and semicircular canals. It contains the **utricle** and **saccule**, which house receptors sensitive to movements of the head.

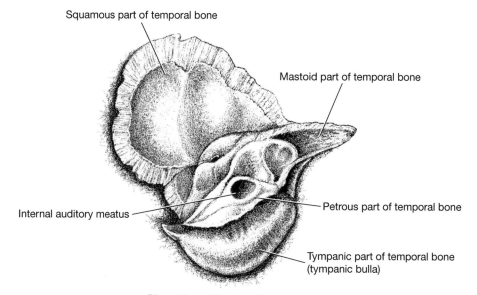

Squamous part of temporal bone

Mastoid part of temporal bone

Internal auditory meatus

Petrous part of temporal bone

Tympanic part of temporal bone
(tympanic bulla)

Dissection of Temporal Bone

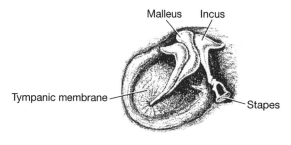

Malleus   Incus

Tympanic membrane

Stapes

The Middle Ear

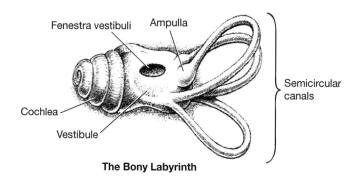

Fenestra vestibuli   Ampulla

Semicircular
canals

Cochlea

Vestibule

The Bony Labyrinth

Figure 8.8 – Ear structures.

CHAPTER REVIEW

A. Answer the following multiple-choice questions by circling the most correct answer.

1. The brain and spinal cord are organs within the
    a. cranial cavity
    c. central nervous system
    b. peripheral nervous system
    d. csf

2. The dura mater is the outermost of the
    a. layers of the brain
    c. spinal cord regions
    b. meninges
    d. cerebrum

3. The convoluted mass that forms most of the forebrain is the
    a. cerebrum
    c. thalamus
    b. cerebellum
    d. hypothalamus

4. The small component of the diencephalon that manages involuntary actions is the
    a. thalamus
    c. pons
    b. hypothalamus
    d. cerebral cortex

5. A thick, transverse band of white matter connecting the two cerebral hemispheres is called the
    a. corpus callosum
    c. central sulcus
    b. longitudinal fissure
    d. cerebellum

6. The tectum and cerebral peduncles are parts of the
    a. forebrain
    c. midbrain
    b. hindbrain
    d. cerebrum

7. The vermis, folia, and arbor vitae may be found within the
    a. cerebellum
    c. forebrain
    b. cerebrum
    d. midbrain

8. The H-shaped mass of tissue in the center of the spinal cord is
    a. white matter
    c. covered by meninges
    b. gray matter
    d. continuous with the cerebral cortex

9. The femoral nerve arises from the:
    a. lumbosacral plexus
    c. dorsal rami
    b. cervical plexus
    d. brachial plexus

10. Photoreceptors, called rods and cones, may be found within the
    a. labyrinth
    c. anterior chamber of the eye
    b. retina
    d. tympanic cavity

B. Complete the sentences below by providing the missing terms from the chapter material.

1. The efferent nervous system includes the _____ _____, which routes impulses to smooth muscles and glands.

2. In order to remove the brain from the cranial cavity, you severed the _____ _____, which were attached to the brain stem at 12 different sites on each side of the brain.

3. The primary functional zone of the cerebrum is the outer fringe of gray matter, known as the _____ _____.

4. The midbrain, pons varolii, and medulla oblongata together form the _____ _____.

5. The spinal cord terminates as a slender filament, called the _____ _____, in the base of the tail.

6. The plexus that is located medial to the shoulder and cranial to the 1st rib, and can be observed from the ventral side deep to the pectoral muscles, is the _____ _____.

7. A vertical row of autonomic ganglia extending along both sides of the vertebral column from the base of the skull to the tail describes the _____ _____ _____.

8. Taste receptors are organized into specialized groups of cells, known as the _____ _____.

9. The large oval or spherical structure that is suspended by suspensory ligaments extending from the ciliary body and located behind the pupil is called the _____.

10. The _____ is a coiled, snail-shell-like part of the labyrinth that contains the receptors responsible for audation, known as hair cells.

C. Answer the following descriptive and critical-thinking questions with a brief explanation in the spaces provided.

1. Describe the role of the cerebrum in achieving the functions of the nervous system._____

    _____

    _____

    _____

    _____

    _____

2. Identify the structures that light must pass through in order to stimulate photoreceptors.

_____

_____

_____

_____

_____

_____

3. Describe the pathway of vibrations that result in audation. _____

_____

_____

_____

_____

_____

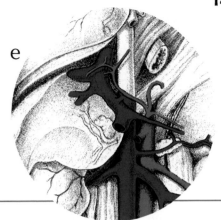

chapter nine

THE ENDOCRINE SYSTEM

The endocrine system works hand in hand with the nervous system to regulate body functions. Like the nervous system, it provides a method of control in order to keep the body functioning, despite changing conditions in the environment. Thus, the primary role of the endocrine system is to achieve homeostasis, a state in which the body's equilibrium is maintained.

The endocrine system communicates to the body by secreting chemicals into the bloodstream. The chemicals are called **hormones**, which are produced by special organs known as endocrine glands. The organs are also called glands because their primary function is the secretion of a product.

Endocrine glands secrete hormones directly into the watery environment surrounding each cell. From there, the hormones enter the bloodstream, which carries them throughout the body's circulation until they reach the part of the body they are to affect. Because blood flows much more slowly than the conduction of a nerve impulse, a hormone takes longer to reach its destination. As a result, the control provided by the endocrine system occurs more slowly, and also lasts longer, when compared to the nervous system.

Structurally, the endocrine system consists of the organs of the body that secrete hormones, which are scattered throughout the body. They include seven primary organs: pituitary gland, pineal gland, thyroid gland, parathyroid glands, adrenal glands, pancreas, and gonads. Several other organs also secrete hormones, although as a secondary function. You have studied them in previous chapters so they will not be considered here; they include the stomach, kidneys, thymus, and heart.

PITUITARY GLAND

The pituitary gland, which is also called the hypophysis, is connected to the hypothalamus at the base of the brain (Figure 9.1). The narrow bridge between the pituitary gland and the hypothalamus is known as the infundibulum. You have identified the pituitary gland during your study of the nervous system (Chapter 8), so you need not observe it again in your cat. The pituitary gland is a small oval gland composed of two parts: the **anterior pituitary** (adenohypophysis) and the **posterior pituitary** (neurohypophysis). It secretes a number of hormones, which are listed in Table 9.1.

PINEAL GLAND

Similar to the pituitary, the pineal gland is located within the cranial cavity. It forms part of the diencephalon, which you identified in Chapter 8 (Figure 9.1). It is a small gland, which produces a hormone (melatonin) that regulates biological cycles. If the brain of your cat is still available to observe, identify the pineal gland as the small caudal projection between the cerebral hemispheres.

THYROID GLAND

The thyroid gland is located caudal to the larynx in the ventral neck region (Figure 9.1). It consists of two **lobes**, right and left, that are often connected near the ventral midline by a thin bridge of fragile tissue called the **isthmus**. The thyroid gland secretes thyroxin, a hormone that regulates the rate of cellular metabolism in all body cells. It also secretes calcitonin, which reduces calcium levels in the bloodstream. Identify the thyroid gland in the neck of your specimen.

PARATHYROID GLANDS

The parathyroid glands are four, or sometimes five, small bodies embedded within the dorsal side of the thyroid gland (Figure 9.1). Because of their small size, they are not evident during routine dissection. The parathyroid glands secrete parathyroid hormone, which increases calcium levels in the bloodstream and is an antagonist to calcitonin.

ADRENAL GLANDS

The adrenal glands are a pair of oval organs, each located ventromedial to a kidney (Figure 9.1). Also known as the suprarenal glands, each consists of an outer **adrenal cortex** that secretes steroid hormones and an inner **adrenal medulla** that secretes epinephrine and norepinephrine. The steroid hormones of the adrenal cortex regulate water balance, reduce inflammation, participate in carbohydrate metabolism, and stimulate sex characteristics and sex cell development. The medullary products supplement the effect of the sympathetic division of the autonomic nervous system. Identify the adrenal glands in your specimen. *The human adrenals actually cap the superior border of the kidneys.*

PANCREAS

You have observed the pancreas in Chapter 4, because it performs digestive functions. Recall that it is an oblong, glandular structure located dorsal to the stomach in the abdominal cavity (Figure 9.1). The endocrine functions of the pancreas are isolated within small clusters of cells surrounded by digestive enzyme-secreting cells. The clusters are known as **islets of Langerhans**. The cells of the islets secrete insulin and glucagon, which regulate glucose (sugar) levels in the bloodstream. Identify the pancreas once again where it lies within the abdominal cavity.

GONADS

The gonads are the testes in the male and the ovaries in the female. You have identified these sexual organs in your study of Chapter 7. They are organs of the endocrine system because their primary function is the secretion of hormones. Recall that the male testes secrete testosterone, and the female ovaries secrete estrogen and progesteron. Identify these endocrine glands in a male and a female cat once again (Figure 9.1).

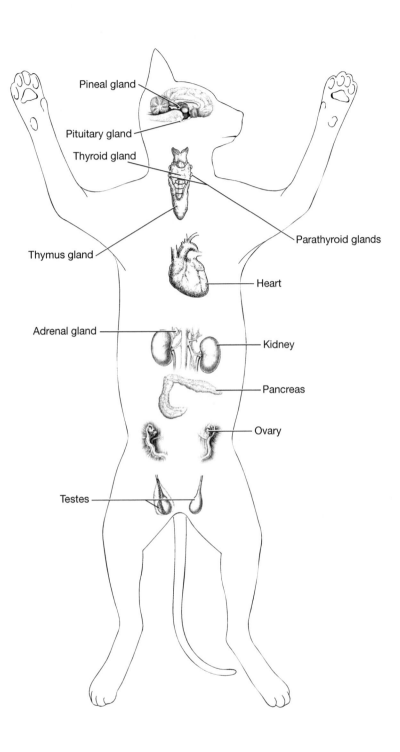

Figure 9.1 – Endocrine glands of the cat.

GLAND	HORMONE SECRETED	PRIMARY EFFECT
Pituitary Gland: Anterior Lobe	Growth hormone (GH) Melanocyte-stimulating hormone (MSH) Prolactin (PRL) Adrenocorticotropic hormone (ACTH) Thyroid-stimulating hormone (TSH) Follicle-stimulating hormone (FSH) Luteinizing hormone (LH) Oxytocin (OT) Antidiuretic hormone (ADH)	Controls growth and development Stimulates melanocytes to increase skin pigmentation Stimulates milk secretion by the mammary glands Stimulates the cortex of the adrenal glands Stimulates the thyroid gland Stimulates development of ove, sperm Stimulates the secretion of sex hormones by the gonads Stimulates contractions of the uterus and the release of milk by mammary glands Stimulates water reabsorption in the kidneys
Posterior Lobe		
Pineal Gland	Melatonin	Regulates body rhythms
Thyroid Gland	Thyroxin (T4) and Triiodothyronin (T3) Calcitonin (CT)	Controls catabolic metabolism and protein synthesis in most body cells Reduces calcium levels in the blood

Adrenal Glands:
  Medulla
 	
  Cortex
	Epinephrine & Norepinephrine
	
	Mineralocorticoids (aldosterone)
	
	Glucocorticoids (cortisol, corticosterone, cortisone)
	
	Sex hormones (androgens & estrogens)
		Prolongs the conditions responsible for the "flight or fight" response
		Maintains fluid balance by stimulating the retention of sodium and excreting potassium; helps regulate blood pressure
		Stimulates glycogen formation and storage, increases body resistance to stress, and reduces inflammation
		Stimulates sex characteristics; stimulates sex cell development

Pancreas (Islets of Langerhans)	Glucagon Insulin	Stimulates the conversion of glycogen to glucose Stimulates the conversion of glucose to glycogen

Gonads:
  Ovaries
 	
  Testes
	Estrogens
	
	Testosterone
		Stimulates development of female sex characteristics, ovarian cycle, and menstrual cycle
		Stimulates development of male sex characteristics, and sperm production

Table 9.1 – Endocrine glands and their hormones

CHAPTER REVIEW

A. Answer the following multiple-choice questions by circling the most correct answer.

1. The chemical messengers of the endocrine system are known as
   a. proteins
   b. electrolytes
   c. hormones
   d. endoglastins

2. The pituitary gland has a direct connection to the
   a. cerebral cortex
   b. hypothalamus
   c. thalamus
   d. pineal gland

3. The pineal gland is located within the
   a. cranial cavity
   b. diencephalon
   c. brain
   d. all of the above

4. The endocrine gland that is located below the larynx in the ventral neck region is the
   a. thalamus
   b. adrenal gland
   c. thyroid gland
   d. pituitary gland

5. The four or five tiny glands that are embedded within the thyroid gland are known as
   a. lymph nodes
   b. parathyroid glands
   c. tumors
   d. pineal glands

6. The glands that may be found ventromedial to each kidney are the
   a. adrenal glands
   b. gastric glands
   c. islets of Langerhans
   d. parathyroid glands

7. The islets of Langerhans are clusters of endocrine cells located within the
   a. hypothalamus
   b. ventral neck region
   c. pancreas
   d. gonads

8. The gonads are endocrine glands because they
   a. produce the gametes
   b. serve reproductive functions
   c. secrete hormones
   d. none of the above

9. Calcium levels in the blood are regulated by the thyroid and
   a. metabolic activity
   b. parathryoid glands
   c. bone cells
   d. adrenal glands

10. Insulin and glucagon are hormones that regulate sugar levels in the blood. They are secreted by endocrine cells within the
    a. pancreas
    b. adrenal cortex
    c. thyroid gland
    d. anterior pituitary gland

B. Complete the sentences below by providing the missing terms from the chapter material.

1. Structurally, the endocrine system consists of the organs of the body that secrete _____.

2. The _____ _____ is connected to the hypothalamus at the base of the brain.

3. The _____ _____ is part of the diencephalon of the brain.

4. The _____ _____ is located on the ventral aspect of the neck.

5. The _____ _____ are tiny glands that are embedded within the thyroid gland.

6. The _____ _____ are located ventromedial to each kidney.

7. The _____ contains clusters of endocrine cells known as islets of Langerhans.

8. The glands that secrete testosterone are the _____.

9. Estrogens are secreted by the _____.

10. The anterior _____ _____ regulates several other endocrine glands.

C. Answer the following descriptive and critical-thinking questions with a brief explanation in the spaces provided.

1. Contrast the primary functional role of the nervous system with that of the endocrine system.

_____

_____

_____

_____

_____

_____

Appendix

ANSWERS TO CHAPTER REVIEWS

CHAPTER ONE

A. 1. d; 2. a; 3. a; 4. c; 5. b; 6. b; 7. d; 8. c; 9. c; 10. a

B. 1. mastoid process; 2. occipital; 3. sphenoid; 4. palatine; 5. maxillary; 6. coronal suture; 7. thoracic; 8. humerus; 9. ilium, ischium; 10. talus

C. 1. The talus is very large, the calcaneus is elongate, the metatarsals are elongate, and the phalanges are angled to support weight.

2. Overall, the human cranium is much larger to accommodate the larger brain. More subtle differences include no distinct presphenoid in the human, and the temporal bone has less distinctive divisions in the human.

3. The innominate bones of the human differ from the cat due to the posture differences of bipedal gait. The innominate bones are in a more upright position in the human, and the ilium has a greater width relative to overall size. Also, the innominate bones are sexually dimorphic in humans; that is, the female ilium flares laterally, while the male ilium is more upright, and the angle between the opposing pubic bones is more obtuse in the female to form the birth canal.

CHAPTER TWO

A. 1. c; 2. d; 3. c; 4. d; 5. d; 6. c; 7. b; 8. b; 9. c; 10. a

B. 1. blunt probe; 2. needle probes; 3. eyelids; 4. pectoral; 5. urogenital; 6. axilla; 7. breasts; 8. cutaneus maximus; 9. platysma; 10. single piece

C. 1. The skin should be retained so that it may be used as a wrap between dissections to reduce dehydration of tissues.

2. Over-use of a scalpel can lead to unnecessary cuts and a greater chance of personal injury during a dissection.

3. Dissection provides experience with touching and seeing real structures, which enhances learning and recall. It also serves to teach dissection skills.

CHAPTER THREE

A. 1. a; 2. b; 3. b; 4. b; 5. c; 6. c; 7. b; 8. a; 9. b; 10. a

B. 1. aponeurosis; 2. fascia; 3. adduction; 4. pectoantebrachialis; 5. trapezius; 6. brachialis; 7. brachioradialis; 8. fascia lata; 9. biceps femoris; 10. serratus ventralis

C. 1. The quadriceps femoris group primarily extends the shank at the knee joint. The four muscles provide great force to enable the quadriped to run and leap by the push downward force that is exerted onto the ground. This force must be even greater in bipeds, because there is no assistance in the action by the fore-limbs.

2. In humans, the gluteus maximus is a much more extensive muscle than the gluteus maximus of quadripeds due to the stepping motion required of the bipedal gait. The g. medius is larger than the g. maximus in the cat and other quadripeds, but smaller that the g. maximus in humans.

3. The human biceps brachii includes two heads of origin, from which its name is derived: a short head at the glenoid fossa and a long head at the coracoid process. The biceps brachii of the cat has only one origin: the glenoid fossa. In both organisms, the action is the same.

CHAPTER FOUR

A. 1. a; 2. c; 3. c; 4. a; 5. d; 6. c; 7. b; 8. b; 9. a; 10. b

B. 1. accessory organs; 2. parietal peritoneum; 3. abdominal cavity; 4. mandibular glands; 5. hard palate; 6. tongue; 7. oropharynx; 8. mesentery; 9. gallbladder; 10. ileocecal

C. 1. The oral cavity tears and chews food (mastication); salivary glands secrete saliva, which begins carbohydrate digestion and lubricates food for swallowing; stomach begins protein digestion; and small intestine finalizes chemical digestion and performs nutrient absorption.

2. The liver secretes bile to assist in fat digestion within the small intestine; the gallbladder provides temporary storage of bile; pancreas secretes a collection of enzymes that participate in chemical digestion within the small intestine.

3. Based on the strict carnivorous diet of cats and the close similarity of GI tract anatomy between cats and humans, it may be suggested that humans are primarily carnivores. The dentition of humans, however, indicates an adaptation to chewing and grinding plant material, suggesting that meat consump-

tion is supplemented with plants, providing evidence that human adaptations point to an omnivorous diet.

CHAPTER FIVE

A. 1. a; 2. b; 3. b; 4. c; 5. b; 6. d; 7. c; 8. b; 9. c; 10. b

B. 1. external respiration; 2. diaphragm; 3. thoracic; 4. primary bronchi; 5. nasal chambers; 6. thyroid cartilage; 7. glottis; 8. alveoli; 9. pleural; 10. apex

C. 1. Respiration includes ventilation, which is composed of inspiration (inhaling) and expiration (exhaling). Inspiration is initiated when respiratory muscles contract, and expiration results when the muscles relax. External respiration is gas exchange between alveoli and capillaries due to pressure differences, resulting in oxygen moving into the bloodstream. Internal respiration is the movement of oxygen molecules from the bloodstream to body tissues.

2. The lungs are composed of tiny air sacs (alveoli), their surrounding capillaries, larger blood vessels, and the bronchial tree. The bronchial tree begins when the primary bronchi divide into secondary bronchi within each lung, then d i v i d e again into tertiary bronchi. The tertiary bronchi eventually divide to form bronchioles, which end in alveolar ducts that contain alveoli.

CHAPTER SIX

A. 1. a; 2. b; 3. c; 4. c; 5. b; 6. b; 7. b; 8. c; 9. b; 10. c

B. 1. capillaries; 2. left ventricle; 3. right atrium; 4. brachiocephalic artery; 5. caudal vena cava; 6. ventricles; 7. external jugular veins; 8. radial artery; 9. celiac trunk; 10. hepatic portal circulation

C. 1. Right atrium through tricuspid valve to right ventricle, through pulmonary valve to pulmonary trunk and pulmonary circuit, pulmonary veins to left atrium, through bicuspid valve to left ventricle, through aortic valve to aorta.

2. A portal system shunts blood from one capillary network to another, whereas a normal venous system carries blood from a capillary network toward the heart. The hepatic portal circuit shunts blood from the digestive tract to the liver for processing before it enters the general circulation.

3. The aortic branches are, from proximal to distal, the brachiocephalic artery, left subclavian artery, celiac trunk, superior mesenteric artery, adrenolumbar arteries, renal arteries, gonadal arteries, caudal mesenteric artery, lumbar arteries, deep circumflex iliac arteries, external iliac artery, internal iliac artery

CHAPTER SEVEN

A. 1. b; 2. a; 3. b; 4. b; 5. a; 6. b; 7. c; 8. b; 9. c; 10. b

B. 1. nephrons; 2. renal pelvis; 3. trigone; 4. urethra; 5. scrotum; 6. seminiferous tubules; 7. vas deferens; 8. ovarian ligament; 9. uterine horns; 10. urogenital aperture

C. 1. The nephrons are located in the renal cortex and extend into the renal medulla of a kidney. They filter blood, reabsorb water from the filtrate, and secrete excess ions in the formation of urine. Urine formation helps manage blood pressure, fluid and salt balance in body fluids, and eliminates metabolic waste materials.

2. Spermatozoa are produced within seminiferous tubules of the testes, then pass into the ductus epididymus, then into the vas deferens, then into the ejaculatory duct of the urethra. The urethra opens to the exterior via the urogenital orifice.

3. The human vulva contains two pairs of labia, majora and minora, rather than a single pair as seen in the cat. Also, the human clitoris is a more prominent structure. Finally, the urethra and vagina enter the vulva as separate openings in human females: as the urethral orifice and the vaginal orifice.

CHAPTER EIGHT

A. 1. c; 2. b; 3. a; 4. b; 5. a; 6. c; 7. a; 8. b; 9. a; 10. b

B. 1. autonomic system; 2. cranial nerves; 3. cerebral cortex; 4. brain stem; 5. filum terminale; 6. brachial plexus; 7. sympathetic trunk ganglia; 8. taste buds; 9. lens; 10. cochlea

C. 1. The cerebrum consists of the cerebral cortex, which receives sensory information, processes it by interpretation and correlation with memory, and initiates motor responses in order to maintain homeostasis. It also manages consciousness.

2. Light passes through the conjunctiva, then the anterior cavity with aqueous humor, then the pupil, then the lens, then the posterior cavity with aqueous humor, then the choroid, then the retina to stimulate rod and cone cells embedded within the retina.

3. A mechanical vibration is collected by the pinna (auricle) and directed into the external auditory meatus to contact the tympanic membrane, which vibrates in response. This vibration is transmitted to the ossicles: malleus, incus, and stapes, then to the oval window and into the cochlea. The vibration forms waves in fluid, which passes over hair cells to stimulate the impulse.

CHAPTER NINE

A. 1. c; 2. b; 3. d; 4. c; 5. b; 6. a; 7. c; 8. c; 9. b; 10. a

B. 1. hormones; 2. pituitary gland; 3. pineal gland; 4. thyroid gland; 5. parathyroid glands; 6. adrenal glands; 7. pancreas; 8. testes; 9. ovaries; 10. pituitary gland

C.   The nervous system relies upon nerve impulses to convey information from one part of the body to another. The nerve impulses move very rapidly, bringing about change in an instant. In contrast, the endocrine system relies upon the secretion of hormones, their movement into the bloodstream, and the delivery of hormones by way of blood flow. Consequently, hormone action to maintain homeostasis is much slower, and tends to last longer, than nervous action.

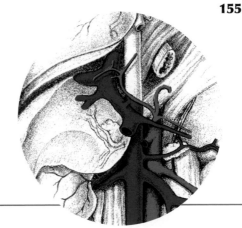

a p p e n d i x

GLOSSARY

A

Abdomen (AB-do-men): The regional area between the diaphragm and pelvis.

Abdominal cavity: The membrane-bound space between the diaphragm, abdominal wall, and pelvis.

Abdominopelvic (ab-do'-mi-no-PEL-vik) **cavity:** The membrane-bound space that includes the abdominal cavity and pelvic cavity.

Abduction (ab-DUK-shun): Movement away from the midline.

Absorption (ab-SORB-shun): The passage of digested foods from the digestive tract and into the bloodstream.

Acetabulum (a'-se-TAB-yoo-lum): A cup-shaped depression on the lateral surface of the coxal (hip) bone. It receives the head of the femur to form the hip joint.

Achilles (a-KIL-es) **tendon:** Also called the calcaneous tendon, it is the common tendon of the calf muscles that originates from the calcaneus (heel).

Adduction (ad-DUK-shun): Movement toward the midline.

Adipose (AD-i-pos): A type of loose connective tissue containing adipocytes, or fat cells.

Adrenal cortex (a-DRE-nal KOR-teks): The outer region of the adrenal glands, located superior to each kidney. It secretes steroid hormones, including glucocorticoids and mineralocorticoids.

Adrenal glands: Two endocrine glands, each situated superior to a kidney. Also called suprarenal glands.

Adrenal medulla: The inner region of the adrenal glands, which secretes epinephrine and nor-epinephrine.

Adventitia (ad'-ven-TISH-ya): The outermost covering of an organ or tissue.

Alimentary canal (a'-li-MEN-ta-re ca-NAL): The tube of the digestive system that includes the mouth, esophagus, stomach, small intestine, and large intestine. Also called the digestive tract, and gastrointestinal (GI) tract.

Alveolar (al-VE-o-lar) **duct:** A branch of a respiratory bronchiole within the lungs that leads to alveoli and alveolar sacs.

Alveolar sac: Two or more alveoli that share a common opening from an alveolar duct.

Alveolus (al-VE-o-lus): alveoli plural form: A microscopic air sac within the lungs.

Amylase (AM-i-las): An enzyme produced by the salivary glands and pancreas that cleaves starch, glycogen, and other polysaccharides during chemical digestion.

Anatomical (a-na-TOM-ik-al) **position:** The reference position, in which the bipedal subject is standing erect with the feet facing forward, arms are at the sides, and the palms of the hands are facing forward (the thumbs are to the outside).

Anatomy (a-NA-to-me): The study of the structure of the body.

Anterior (an-TER-e-or): Toward the belly or front of the body. In humans, it is also called ventral.

Anterior horn: A region of the spinal cord gray matter containing the cell bodies of m o t o r neurons. It is also called the ventral horn.

Anterior root: The structure emerging from the spinal cord on its anterior aspect that contains axons of motor neurons. It is also called the ventral root.

Anterior pituitary gland: The portion of the pituitary gland at the base of the brain composed of glandular epithelium.

Anus (A-nus): The distal end and outlet of the rectum.

Aorta (a-OR-ta): The main trunk of the systemic circulatory circuit. It originates from the left ventricle of the heart.

Aortic semilunar valve: One of four heart valves, it consists of three cusps that are attached to the wall of the aorta near its origin from the left ventricle. It is also called the aortic valve.

Apex (A-peks): The extremity of a conical or pyramidal structure. The apex of the heart is the rounded, inferior-most tip that points to the left side.

Aponeurosis (ap'-o-noo-RO-sis): A broad, sheet-like tendon joining one muscle with another or with a bone.

Appendicular (ap'-en-DIK-yoo-lar): Pertaining to the major appendages, the forelimbs and hindlimbs.

Aqueous humor (AK-we-us HYOO-mor): The watery fluid that fills the anterior compartment of the eye.

Arachnoid (a-RAK-noyd): The middle of three connective tissue coverings (meninges) of the brain and spinal cord.

Areolar (a-RE-o-lar): A type of connective tissue with sparse protein fibers in the matrix (loose connective tissue).

Arrector pili (a-REK-tor Pi-le): Smooth muscle fibers attached to hair within the skin.

Arteriole (ar-TE-re-ol): A small tributary from a larger artery that delivers blood to a capillary.

Artery (AR-ter-e): A blood vessel that carries blood away from the heart.

Articular cartilage (ar-TI-kyoo-lar KAR-ti-lej): The cartilage that covers the end of a bone where it forms a joint with another bone.

Articulation (ar-tik'-yoo-LA-shun): A synonym for joint, which is a point of contact between two opposing bones.

Ascending colon (a-SEN-ding KO-lon): A segment of the large intestine that extends from the cecum to the transverse colon.

Atrioventricular (a-tre-o-ven-TRIK-yoo-lar) **node:** A cluster of specialized cardiac (heart) cells in the right atrial wall that serve as part of the heart conduction system.

Atrioventricular (AV) valve: Two of four heart valves, each of which is located between an atrium and a ventricle. The right AV valve is also called the tricuspid valve, and the left AV valve is also called the bicuspid or mitral valve.

Atrium (A-tre-um): One of two superior chambers of the heart. Plural form is atria.

Audation (ah-DA-shun): The sense of hearing.

Auditory ossicles (AH-di-tor-e OS-ik-elz): The three small bones within the middle ear that transmit sound vibrations: the malleus, incus, and stapes.

Autonomic ganglion (ah'-to-NOM-ik GANG-le-on): A cluster of neuron cell bodies that lie outside the central nervous system, serving either the sympathetic or parasympathetic divisions.

Autonomic nervous system (ANS): A division of the peripheral nervous system that serves body functions not requiring conscious control. It is divided into sympathetic and parasympathetic subdivisions.

Axilla (ak-SIL-a): The small depression beneath the arm where it joins the trunk of the body. It is also called the armpit.

Axial (AK-se-al): The body region along the midline, which includes the head, neck, and trunk.

Axon (AK-son): A long process of a neuron that carries a nerve impulse away from the cell body.

B

Basement membrane: A thin layer of extracellular material that underlies epithelium.

Basilar (BAS-i-lar) **membrane:** One of two membranes in the inner ear that form the cochlear duct. It supports the organ of Corti.

Bicuspid (bi-KUS-pid) **valve**: The left atrioventricular (AV) valve of the heart. It is also called the mitral valve.

Bile: A fluid secreted by the liver and stored in the gallbladder. It assists in the digestion of fats within the small intestine.

Blind spot: A region of the retina where no photoreceptive cells are present, due to the exit point of the optic nerve.

Body cavity: A space in the body that is internally lined by a membrane, and contains structures including organs.

Bony labyrinth (BO-ne LAB-e-rinth): The portion of the inner ear that consists of cavities within the temporal bone, forming the vestibule, cochlea, and semicircular canals.

Brachial (BRA-ke-al): Pertaining to the upper arm.

Brachial plexus (BRA-ke-al PLEK-sus): A network of nerves from the anterior rami of spinal nerves C5, C6, C7, C8, and T1. The nerves of the brachial plexus supply the forelimbs.

Brain stem: The inferior portion of the brain that consists of the midbrain, pons, and medulla oblongata.

Bronchial tree (BRONG-ke-al): A portion of the respiratory conduction zone that consists of a series of tubes that branch from the trachea (the primary bronchi), and continue to branch after entering each lung (into secondary and tertiary bronchi).

Bronchiole (BRONG-ke-ol): A series of small tubes that arise as branches from tertiary bronchi within each lung.

Bronchus (BRONG-kus): Any one of the air passageways that carry air between the trachea and the bronchioles. Plural form is bronchi.

Buccal (BUK-al): Pertaining to the mouth or the cheeks.

Bulbourethral (bul'-bo-yoo-RE-thral) **glands**: A pair of small glands in the male reproductive system located inferior to the prostate gland. Its secretions contribute to semen. Also called Cowper's glands.

C

Calcaneous (kal-KA-ne-us): A large tarsal bone (of the foot), it forms the heel.

Calyx (KAL-iks): A cuplike extension of the renal pelvis (of the kidney). Plural form is calyces.

Canaliculus (kan'-a-LIK-yoo-lus): A small channel within compact bone tissue that connects lacunae. Plural form is canaliculi.

Capillary (KAP-i-lar'-e): A microscopic blood vessel that interconnects arterioles with venules. The capillary wall is a single cell layer in thickness, and is the only site of nutrient diffusion between the bloodstream and body cells.

Cardiac (KAR-de-ak) **muscle**: One of three types of muscle tissue. It is characterized by striations and involuntary contractions, and makes up the bulk of the heart wall.

Carpals (KAR-palz): The eight individual bones of the wrist. As a group, the bones of the wrist are referred to as the carpus.

Cartilage (KAR-ti-lej): A type of connective tissue characterized by the presence of a matrix containing a dense distribution of proteins and a thickened ground substance. The matrix is secreted by chondroblasts.

Cartilaginous (kar'-ti-LA'-jin-us) **joint**: One of three types of joints. It is characterized by the presence of cartilage that connects opposing bones.

Cauda equina (KAH-da e-KWI-na): The group of spinal nerves and roots at the inferior end of the spinal cord.

Cecum (SE-kum): The proximal end of the large intestine that receives the ileum of the small intestine.

Cell: The basic living unit of multicellular organisms.

Cell body: The portion of a neuron that contains the nucleus and much of the cytoplasm. Also called the soma.

Central fovea (FO-ve-a): A small depression in the center of the macula lutea of the retina. It contains cone cells (only), and is the area of optimal visual acuity (clearest vision).

Central nervous system (CNS): A major division of the nervous system that contains the brain and spinal cord.

Cephalic (se-FAL-ik): Pertaining to the head region.

Cerebellum (ser'-e-BEL-um): A functional region of the hindbrain located inferior to the cerebrum. It coordinates muscle movement.

Cerebral aqueduct (SER-e-bral AK-we-dukt): A channel through the midbrain containing cerebrospinal fluid. It connects the third and fourth ventricles of the brain.

Cerebral cortex: The outer layer of the cerebrum, which is composed of gray matter.

Cerebrospinal fluid (se-re'-bro-SPI-nal FLOO-id) **(CSF):** A clear fluid produced as a filtrate from blood in the choroid plexuses of the brain. It circulates through the ventricles of the brain, the central canal of the spinal cord, and the subarachnoid space of the brain and spinal cord.

Cerebrum (SER-e-brum): The largest functional region of the brain, it is the convoluted mass that lies superior to all other parts of the brain. It is the main site of integration of sensory and motor impulses.

Cervical (SER-vi-kal): Pertaining to the neck region.

Cervical plexus (PLEK-sus): A branching network of nerves originating from the anterior rami of the first four cervical nerves.

Cervix (SER-viks): The narrow, constricted part of the uterus that lies between the vagina and the body of the uterus.

Chondrocyte (KON-dro-sit): A mature cartilage cell.

Chordae tendineae (KOR-de TEN-din-e-e): Strands of connective tissue in the heart that anchor atrioventricular valves to papillary muscles.

Choroid (KO-royd): Part of the vascular tunic of the eyeball. It lines most of the internal surface of the sclera, thereby forming the middle layer of the wall of the eye.

Choroid plexus (KO-royd PLEK-sus): A mass of specialized capillaries in the ventricles of the brain, from which cerebrospinal fluid is produced.

Chromosome (KRO-mo-som): One of the structures (46 in human cells) within the cell nucleus that contains genetic material. Chromosomes become visible during cell division.

Ciliary body (SIL-e-ar-e BOD-e): Part of the vascular tunic of the eyeball, along with the choroid and iris. It suspends the lens, and consists of the ciliary muscle and ligaments.

Cilia (SIL-e-a): A hair-like process associated with a cell that is a modification of the plasma membrane. Its movement generates a flow of fluid (usually mucus) in the extracellular environment. Singular form is cilium.

Circumduction (ser'-kum-DUK-shun): A movement at a synovial joint such that the distal end of the bone draws a circular path.

Clavicle (KLA-vik-el): One of two bones connecting the sternum and the forelimb. Also called the collarbone.

Clitoris (KLI-tor-is): The female erectile organ located at the anterior junction of the labia minora.

Coccyx (KOK-siks): The fused bones at the end of the vertebral column of the human.

Cochlea (KOK-le-a): The portion of the inner ear that contains the receptors of hearing (the organ of Corti).

Collagen (KOL-a-jen): A protein that is an abundant component of connective tissue.

Colon (KO-lon): The division of the large intestine containing the ascending, transverse, descending, and sigmoid sections.

Common bile duct: A tube extending from the union of the common hepatic duct and the cystic duct to the duodenum (of the small intestine) that transports bile.

Compact bone: One of two types of bone tissue, it is characterized by a dense matrix filled with mineral salts and collagen arranged in lamellae that surround a central osteonic (Haversian) canal. Also called dense bone.

Conchae (KONG-ke): Scroll-like bones in the facial skeleton forming the superior, middle, and inferior shelves and meati of the nasal cavity.

Condyle (KON-dil): A rounded process of a bone.

Cone: A photoreceptor in the retina of the eye that is involved in color vision and high visual acuity.

Conjunctiva (kon'-junk-TE-va): A thin, transparent membrane lining the outer surface of the cornea of the eye and inner surface of the eyelids.

Connective tissue: One of the four basic types of tissue in the body. It is characterized by an abundance of extracellular material with relatively few cells, and functions in the support and binding of body structures.

Conus medullaris (KO-nus med'-yoo-LAR-is): The tapered terminal end of the spinal cord.

Cornea (KOR-ne-a): The transparent, anterior portion of the fibrous tunic covering the eye.

Coronal (ko-RO-nal) **plane:** A plane that extends vertically to divide the body into anterior and posterior portions. Also called the frontal plane.

Coronary circulation (KO-ro-nar-e ser'-kyoo-LA-shun): The circulatory pathway of blood to the heart wall from the aorta (by way of coronary arteries) and its return to the right atrium (by way of coronary veins).

Coronary sinus: An expanded venous channel on the posterior surface of the heart into which coronary veins empty.

Corpus callosum (KOR-pus ka-LO-sum): A bundle of nerve fibers forming a band of white matter that interconnects the two cerebral hemispheres of the brain.

Corpus luteum (LOO-te-um): A structure within the ovary that forms from a ruptured Graafian follicle and functions as an endocrine gland by secreting female hormones.

Cortex (KOR-teks): The outer portion of an organ.

Costal cartilage (KOS-tel CAR-ti-lej): A band of hyaline cartilage that connects a true rib with the sternum.

Coxal bones (KOK-sal bonz): The two bones that form the pelvis. Also called os coxae, or innominate bones.

Cranial cavity (KRA-ne-al CAV-i-te): The cavity within the skull that contains the brain.

Cranial nerve: One of twelve pairs of nerves that originate from the brain.

Cranium (KRA-ne-um): The skeletal portion of the skull that forms the cranial cavity.

Cystic duct (SIS-tik dukt): A tube that transports bile from the gallbladder to the common bile duct.

Cytoplasm (SI-to-plazm): The material of a cell located within the plasma membrane and outside the nuclear membrane, and containing the cellular organelles.

Cytosol (SI-to-sol): The thickened fluid of the cytoplasm that lies outside the cellular organelle membranes.

Cytoskeleton (ci'-to-SKEL-e-ton): A complex supportive network of microtubules and microfilaments within the cytoplasm of a cell.

D

Deep: A directional term meaning away from the surface of the body.

Deep fascia (FASH-e-a): A sheet of connective tissue covering the external surface of a muscle. Also called the epimysium.

Defecation (def'-e-CA-shun): The discharge of feces from the rectum through the anus. Also called elimination.

Dendrite (DEN-drit): A cytoplasmic extension from the cell body of a neuron that carries a nerve impulse toward the cell body.

Deoxyribonucleic acid (de-ok'-se-ri-bo-nyoo-KLE-ik A-sid) (DNA): A nucleic acid in the shape of a double helix that contains the genetic information necessary for protein synthesis.

Depression (de-PRE-shun): Movement of a body part downward.

Dermis (DER-mis): The layer of the skin lying deep to the epidermis and composed of dense, irregular connective tissue.

Descending colon (de-SEN-ding KO-lon): The segment of the large intestine between the transverse colon and the sigmoid colon.

Diaphragm (DI-a-fram): An internal, circular muscle dividing the thoracic cavity from the abdominopelvic cavity.

Diaphysis (di-A-fi-sis): The shaft of a long bone.

Diastole (di-AS-to-le): A part of the cardiac cycle characterized by relaxation of the heart chambers, during which they fill with blood.

Diencephalon (di-en-CEF-a-lon): A region of the brain located inferior to the cerebrum. It is part of the forebrain, and contains the thalamus, hypothalamus, and pineal gland.

Digestion (di-JES-chun): The breakdown of food particles into units small enough to be absorbed.

Digestive tract: (see Alimentary canal).

Dilate (DI-lat): To enlarge in size or expand.

Distal (DIS-tal): A directional term identifying a body part located further from the origin or point of attachment to the trunk relative to another.

Distal convoluted tubule: A segment of the renal tubule (of the kidney nephron) that extends from the loop of Henle to the collecting duct.

Dorsal (DOR-sal): A directional term indicating toward the back side, or posterior.

Dorsal cavity: A major body cavity containing the cranial cavity and the vertebral canal.

Dorsal root: The sensory branch of a spinal nerve that connects with the spinal cord.

Dorsiflexion (dor'-se-FLEK-shun): Movement of the foot toward the dorsal side.

Ductus deferens (DUK-tus DEF-er-enz): The tube that conducts sperm from the epididymis in the testes to the ejaculatory duct. Also called vas deferens and seminal duct.

Duodenum (doo-o-DE-num): The first segment of the small intestine that extends from the pyloric valve to the jejunum.

Dura mater (DYOO-ra MA-ter): The outer of the three meninges that surround the brain and spinal cord.

E

Effector (e-FEK-tor): Any muscle or gland that responds to a stimulus from a motor neuron.

Efferent arteriole (EF-er-ent ar-TE-re-ol): An arteriole that transports blood away from the glomerulus of a nephron (in the kidney).

Efferent ductules (DUK-tyoo-elz): Small coiled tubes that transport sperm from the rete testis to the epididymis.

Efferent neuron (NOO-ron): A neuron that carries impulses away from the central nervous system. Also called motor neuron.

Ejaculation (e-jak'-yoo-LA-shun): The expulsion of semen from the penis, which is accomplished by reflexive muscle contractions.

Ejaculatory duct (e-JAK-yoo-la-to-re dukt): A short tube that carries sperm from the ductus deferens to the urethra.

Electrolyte (e-LEK-tro-lit): A chemical that can separate into ions and conduct an electric current when in a water solution.

Elevation (el-e-VA-shun): Movement of a body part upward.

Embryo (EM-bre-o): In the human, it is the developing organism during its first eight weeks of life following fertilization.

Endocardium (en-do-KAR-de-um): The inner layer of the heart wall that forms a thin, smooth lining covering the chambers and valves.

Endochondral ossification (en-do-KON-dral os'-i-fi-KA-shun): The development of bone such that bone tissue forms in replacement of hyaline cartilage.

Endocrine gland (EN-do-krin gland): One of two main categories of glands, in which the products are secreted into the extracellular space and transported by the bloodstream. Also called ductless glands.

Endocytosis (en'-do-si-TO-sis): The active process of bulk transport of material into a cell. It includes phagocytosis and pinocytosis.

Endolymph (EN-do-lymf): The fluid within the membranous labyrinth of the inner ear.

Endometrium (en'-do-ME-tre-um): The inner, vascular layer of the uterus.

Endomysium (en'-do-MI-se-um): The deepest layer of connective tissue associated with a muscle. It surrounds individual muscle fibers.

Endoneurium (en'-do-NYOO-re-um): The deepest layer of connective tissue associated with a nerve. It surrounds individual nerve fibers (myelinated axons of neurons).

Endoplasmic reticulum (en'-do-PLAZ-mik re-TIK-yoo-lum) (ER): A cytoplasmic organelle that consists of a series of tubules with a hollow center. It functions in the transport of cellular products (smooth ER), and as a site for protein synthesis (if ribosomes are attached, called rough ER).

Endosteum (en-DO-ste-um): A membrane lining the medullary cavity within a bone and containing osteoblasts and osteoclasts.

Endothelium (en'-do-THE-le-um): A layer of simple squamous epithelium lining the inside of blood vessels and the heart chambers.

Enzyme (EN-zim): A protein that performs the role of catalyst in a chemical reaction.

Eosinophil (e'-o-SIN-o-fil): A type of granulated white blood cell characterized by a cytoplasm that accepts the eosin stain.

Ependymal (e-pen-DI-mal) **cells**: A type of neuroglial cell in the brain that lines the ventricles. Also called ependymocytes.

Epicardium (ep'-i-KAR-de-um): The thin outer layer of the heart wall. Also called the visceral pericardium.

Epidermis (ep'-i-DERM-is): The superficial layer of skin composed of stratified squamous epithelium.

Epididymis (ep'-i-DID-i-mis): An organ in the male reproductive system that consists of a coiled tube located within the scrotum.

Epiglottis (ep'-i-GLOT-is): A part of the larynx that consists of a leaf-shaped piece of hyaline cartilage that forms a movable lid over the opening into the trachea, called the glottis.

Epimysium (ep'-i-MI-ze-um): The outer layer of connective tissue associated with muscle, it surrounds the whole muscle. Also called deep fascia.

Epineurium (ep'-i-NYOO-re-um): The outermost layer of connective tissue associated with a nerve. It surrounds the whole nerve.

Epiphyseal (ep'-i-FIZ-e-al) **line**: A line of calcified bone visible in a section through bone that is the remnant of the epiphyseal plate.

Epiphyseal plate: A region of cartilage between the epiphysis and diaphysis that produces lengthwise growth of a bone.

Epiphysis (e-PIF-i-sis): The end of a long bone that contains spongy bone tissue.

Epithelial (ep'-i-THE-le-al) **tissue**: One of four primary tissue types, it is characterized by a close arrangement of cells with little intercellular material. Also called epithelium.

Eponychium (ep'-o-NIK-e-um): A narrow region of stratum corneum at the proximal end of a nail. Also called cuticle.

Erythrocyte (e-RITH-ro-sit): A synonym for red blood cell.

Erythropoiesis (e-rith'-ro-poy-E-sis): The process by which erythrocytes are formed.

Esophagus (e-SOF-a-gus): A tubular segment of the alimentary canal between the pharynx and the stomach.

Eustachian (yoo-STA-she-an) **tube**: See auditory tube.

Eversion (e-VER-zhun): Movement of the sole of the foot in an outward direction.

Exocrine (EK-so-krin) **gland**: One of two main categories of glands, in which the products are released into ducts that transport them to the body surface or into body cavities.

Exocytosis (ek'-so-si-TO-sis): The active cellular process by which materials are transported out of a cell and into the extracellular environment.

Expiration (ek'-spi-RA-shun): The process of expelling air from the lungs to the external environment, or breathing out. Also called exhalation.

Extension (ek-STEN-shun): Movement of a body part such that the angle between opposing bones is increased; returning to original position after flexion.

External auditory canal: The epidermal-lined tube of the external ear extending from the auricle to the tympanic membrane. It passes through the hole in the temporal bone called the external auditory meatus.

External ear: The outer part of the ear, which consists of the appendage known as the auricle, the external auditory canal, and the tympanic membrane.

External nares (NAR-ez): The openings of the nose between the external environment and the nasal cavity. Also called nostrils.

External respiration: The exchange of respiratory gases between the lungs and the bloodstream.

Extracellular environment (ek'-stra-CEL-yoo-lar en-VI-ron-ment): The body space outside the plasma membrane of cells.

Extracellular fluid (ECF): The fluid outside the plasma membrane of cells, including interstitial fluid and blood plasma.

F

Facet (FA-set): A smooth articular surface on a bone.

Falciform ligament (FAL-si-form LIG-a-ment): A part of the parietal peritoneum that is located between the right and left lobes of the liver.

Fallopian tube (see Uterine tube).

Fascia (FASH-e-a): A sheet or band of dense connective tissue that structurally supports organs and tissues. Deep fascia surrounds muscle, and superficial fascia separates the skin and muscle layers.

Fascicle (FAS-i-kul): A bundle of skeletal muscle fibers (cells) that forms a part of a muscle.

Fat: A lipid compound formed from one molecule of glycerol and three molecules of fatty acids. It is the body's most concentrated form of energy, and also serves to insulate from external temperature changes. It is stored within cells comprising adipose tissue.

Fauces (FAW-ses): The opening into the pharynx from the oral cavity (mouth).

Feces (FE-sez): Waste material discharged from the large intestine during defecation.

Fertilization (fer'-ti-li-ZA-shun): The union of a sperm cell with a secondary oocyte.

Fetus (FE-tus): The early developmental stage from eight weeks after fertilization to the time of birth.

Fibroblast (FI-bro-blast): A large cell in connective tissue that manufactures much of the intercellular material.

Fibrous (FI-brus) **joint:** One of three general types of joints in the body. Fibrous joints are characterized by the presence of dense connective tissue between opposing bones. They allow little or no movement between bones.

Fibrous tunic: The outer wall of the eyeball that is composed of dense connective tissue, it contains the sclera and the cornea.

Filum terminale (FI-lum ter-mi-NAL-e): Connective tissue that extends beyond the conus medullaris of the spinal cord inferiorly into the coccyx.

Fimbriae (FIM-bre-e): The fingerlike extensions of the uterine tube at its proximal end (near the ovary).

Fissure (FISH-er): A cleft or groove separating two parts, such as the cerebral hemispheres of the brain; a deep sulcus of the brain.

Flagellum (fla-JEL-um): A single, long extension of a cell composed of protein filaments to provide mobility. In human cells, it is found only in sperm cells.

Flexion (FLEK-shun): Movement of a body part such that the angle between bones is decreased.

Foramen (fo-RA-men): An opening or passage through bone. Plural form is foramina.

Foramen magnum (MAG-num): The large opening at the base of the skull through which passes the spinal cord.

Fossa (FOS-a): A shallow depression or groove in a bone.

Fourth ventricle (forth VEN-tri-kul): The cavity in the brain located between the cerebellum and the midbrain and pons.

Fovea centralis (FO-ve-a cen-TRAL-is): The region of the retina that consists of cone cells, but no rod cells; it is the area of highest visual acuity (sharpness of vision).

Frontal plane: A plane that extends in a verticle direction dividing the human body into front (anterior) and back (posterior) portions. Also called the coronal plane.

G

Gallbladder (GAWL-blad-er): A small saclike organ located beneath the liver that stores bile.

Gamete (ga-MET): A sex cell. It may be male (sperm cell) or female (oocyte).

Ganglion (GANG-le-on): A cluster of neuron cell bodies located outside the central nervous system.

Gastric (GAS-trik) **gland**: Any one of several types of glands in the stomach mucosa that contributes to the gastric juice.

Gene: A segment of a DNA molecule that contains the information needed to synthesize one complete polypeptide chain.

Genitalia (jen'-i-TAL-ya): The reproductive organs.

Germinal (JER-mi-nal) **epithelium**: A layer of epithelial cells covering the ovaries.

Gestation (jes-TA-shun): The period of development prior to birth.

Gingivae (jin-JI-ve): The mucous membrane covering the alveolar processes of the m a x i l - lary bones and mandible. Also called the gums.

Gland: A specialization of epithelial tissue to secrete substances. It may consist of a single cell or a multicellular arrangement.

Glans penis (glanz PE-nis): The slightly enlarged, distal end of the penis.

Glomerulus (glo-MER-yoo-lus): One of many specialized capillary networks located in the kidney cortex, each of which is encapsulated by a Bowman's capsule. It is part of the kidney nephron, and is the site of kidney filtration.

Glottis (GLOT-is): The opening into the larynx from the pharynx.

Glucose (GLOO-kos): A monosaccharide that serves as the preferred energy source by the body.

Glycogen (GLI-ko-jen): A polysaccharide composed of glucose subunits that is manufactured by the liver to serve as a storage form of energy.

Goblet cell: A unicellular gland, often in the shape of a goblet, that secretes mucus. Also called a mucus cell.

Golgi apparatus (GOL-je ap'-a-RAT-us): A cellular organelle characterized by a series of flattened, hollow cisternae. It serves as a site of anabolic activities.

Gonad (GO-nad): An organ that produces gametes and sex hormones. In the male it is the testes, and in the female it is the ovaries.

Gray matter: Nerve tissue in the brain and spinal cord that contains neuron cell bodies, dendrites, and nonmyelinated axons, and therefore appears gray or non-white in color.

Greater omentum (GRA-ter o-MEN-tum): A large fold of the serosa of the stomach (or visceral peritoneum) that covers over the abdominal cavity.

Groin (groyn): The region of the body located between the thigh and the trunk.

Gustation (gus-TA-shun): The sense of taste.

Gyrus (JI-rus): An upfolding convolution on the cerebral surface of the brain. Plural is gyri.

H

Hair: A threadlike outgrowth of the skin that is composed of columns of keratinized cells.

Hair follicle: A cluster of epithelial tissue surrounding the root of a hair where the hair originates.

Hard palate (PAL-at): The anterior portion of the roof of the mouth. It is formed by the maxillary and palatine bones and is lined with mucous membrane.

Haustra (HAWS-tra): The pouches in the large intestine that form when the taenia coli muscle contracts.

Haversian system (see Osteon).

Head: The region of the body superior to the neck. The rounded, proximal end of a long bone. The proximal attachment of a muscle to a bone.

Heart: The hollow muscular organ within the thoracic cavity that propels blood through the circulatory network.

Hematopoiesis (hem'-a-to-poy-E-sis): The production of blood cells in the red bone marrow. Also called hemopoiesis.

Hemoglobin (he'-mo-GLO-bin): A complex protein in red blood cells involved in the transport of oxygen and carbon dioxide.

Hepatic (he-PAT-ic): Pertaining to the liver.

Hepatic portal circulation: A circulatory network within the systemic system that involves the transport of blood from the alimentary canal to the liver. Its main vessel is the hepatic portal vein.

Hilum (HI-lum): An area of an organ, usually a depression, where blood vessels and nerves enter or exit. Also called a hilus.

Histology (HIS-to-lo-je): The microscopic study of tissues.

Homeostasis (ho'-me-o-STA-sis): A condition of equilibrium, or physiological stability, of body systems, in which the internal environment of the body remains relatively constant.

Homologous (ho-MOL-o-gus): Two organs that correspond in structure, position, and origin.

Horizontal plane: A plane that extends perpendicular to the length of the body, dividing it into superior and inferior portions. Also called transverse plane.

Hormone (HOR-mon): A substance secreted by endocrine tissue that changes the physiological activity of the target cell.

Hypodermis (hi'-po-DERM-is): The area of the body between the dermis of the skin and skeletal muscle.

Hypothalamus (hi'-po-THAL-a-mus): The small, inferior portion of the diencephalon in the brain. It functions mainly in the control of involuntary activities, including endocrine gland regulation, sleep, thirst, and hunger.

I

Ileocecal valve (il'-e-o-SE-kal valv): A fold of mucous membrane between the ileum (of the small intestine) and the cecum (of the large intestine). Also called the ileocecal sphincter.

Ileum (IL-e-um): The distal segment of the small intestine.

Inferior (in-FER-e-or): A directional term describing a location further from the head than something else.

Infundibulum (in'-fun-DIB-yoo-lum): The narrow connection between the hypothalamus of the brain and the pituitary gland. Also, the funnel-shaped distal end of the uterine tube that opens near an ovary.

Ingestion (in-GES-chun): The intake of food or liquid by the mouth.

Inguinal (IN-gwi-nal): Pertaining to the groin region (between the hip and thigh).

Insertion (in-SER-shun): The attachment of a muscle by its tendon to a movable bone.

Inspiration (in-spi-RA-shun): The act of drawing air into the lungs. Also called inhalation.

Integumentary (in-teg'-yoo-MEN-tar-e): Pertaining to the skin and its accessory organs.

Intercalated disk (in-ter'-ka-LA-ted disk): A transverse thickening of a cardiac muscle cell's sarcolemma at its boundary with an adjacent cell. It aids in the conduction of an impulse from one cardiac cell to another.

Intercellular (in'-ter-SEL-yoo-lar) **environment:** The area between cells.

Internal (in-TER-nal): A directional term describing a location deep to the surface of the skin relative to something else.

Internal nares (NAR-ez): The paired openings between the nasal cavity and the nasopharynx through which air passes. Also called choanae.

Internal respiration: The exchange of respiratory gases between the blood and body cells.

Interstitial cells (in'-ter-STI-shul): Cells in the testes located between seminiferous tubules that secrete testosterone. Also called cells of Leydig.

Interstitial fluid (in'-ter-STI-shul FLOO-id): The portion of extracellular fluid that fills the tissue spaces between cells. Also called tissue fluid and intercellular fluid.

Intervertebral disk (in'-ter-VER-te-bral disk): A cartilaginous joint that consists of a pad of fibrocartilage located between two adjacent vertebrae.

Intestinal gland (in-TES-tin-al gland): A tubular gland in the mucosa of the small intestine that secretes digestive enzymes. Also called crypt of Leiberkuhn.

Intracellular (in'-tra-SEL-yoo-lar) **environment:** The space within a cell.

Intracellular fluid (ICF): The fluid within cells.

Intramembranous ossification (in'-tra-MEM-bra-nus os'-i-fi-KA-shun): The development of bone from fetal connective tissue membranes.

Invagination (in-vaj'-in-A-shun): A folding inward of a body cavity wall into the body cavity.

Inversion (in-VER-zhun): Movement of the foot inward such that the sole of the foot faces medially.

In vitro (in VE-tro): Outside the body, such as in a culture bottle.

In vivo (in VE-vo): Inside the living body.

Iris (I-ris): A part of the vascular tunic of the eye. It is located on the anterior side of the eyeball and is composed of smooth muscle fibers that regulate the amount of light entering the eye. The iris is the colored part of the eye surrounding the pupil.

Islet of Langerhans (I-let of LANG-er-hanz): One of numerous clusters of endocrine cells within the pancreas.

J

Jejunum (je-JOO-num): The middle segment of the small intestine.

Joint (joynt): A point of contact between two opposing bones. Also called articulation.

Juxtaglomerular apparatus (juks'-ta-glo-MER-yoo-lar ap'-a-RAT-us): A structure located in a kidney nephron that is composed of cells from the distal convoluted tubule and the afferent arteriole. It secretes renin in response to a decrease in blood pressure.

K

Keratin (KER-a-tin): A waterproofing protein present in the epidermis, nails, and hair.

L

Labium (LA-be-um): A synonym for lip. Plural form is labia.

Labyrinth (LAB-i-rinth): The system of interconnecting tubes of the inner ear.

Lacrimal (LAK-ri-mal): Pertaining to the production or release of tears.

Lactation (lak-TA-shun): The production of milk by the mammary glands.

Lacteal (lak-TE-al): A small lymphatic vessel located within a villus of the small intestine that transports fat.

Lacuna (la-KOO-na): A chamber within bone or cartilage matrix that houses a cell (an osteocyte or chondrocyte). Plural form is lacunae.

Lamellae (la-MEL-e): Concentric rings of hardened bone matrix found in compact bone.

Large intestine: The final segment of the alimentary canal consisting of a large tube that forms the feces, which is expelled by the process of defecation.

Laryngopharynx (la-ring'-o-FAR-inks): The inferior part of the pharynx, which opens to the esophagus (posteriorly) and to the larynx (anteriorly).

Larynx (LAR-inks): A box-like cartilaginous organ in the respiratory tract located between the pharynx and the trachea.

Lateral (LA-ter-al): A directional term describing a structure that is located further from the vertical midline of the body relative to another.

Lens: An oval, transparent structure located between the posterior iris and the vitreous humor of the eyeball. It is connected to the vascular tunic by suspensory ligaments.

Lesser omentum (LES-er o-MEN-tum): A fold of the peritoneum that extends between the liver and the medial margin of the stomach.

Leukocyte (LOO-ko-sit): A white blood cell. Also called leucocyte.

Ligament (LIG-a-ment): A band or cord of dense connective tissue that extends from one bone to another to provide a joint with structural stability.

Lingual (LIN-gwal): Pertaining to the tongue; for example, the lingual frenulum that connects the tongue to the floor of the mouth.

Lipid (LI-pid): An organic compound that is usually insoluble in water, but soluble in alcohol, ether, and chloroform. It includes fats, phospholipids, and steroids.

Liver: A large digestive organ in the superior right corner of the abdominopelvic cavity that functions mainly in the interconversion of energy-storage molecules, detoxification of blood, and production of bile.

Lumbar (LUM-bar): The region of the back between the ribs and pelvis. Also called loins.

Lumen (LOO-men): The potential space within a tubular structure.

Lung: One of two large organs in the thoracic cavity that functions in the exchange of respiratory gases.

Lymph (limf): The slow-moving fluid within lymphatic vessels of the lymphatic system.

Lymph node: A small, oval organ located within the lymphatic vessel network.

Lymphatic tissue: A specialized type of connective tissue that contains an abundance of lymphocytes. Also called lymphoid tissue.

Lymphatic vessel: A hollow tubular structure similar to a vein that transports lymph in a direction leading toward the heart.

Lymphocyte (LIM-fo-cit): A type of white blood cell lacking large granules in the cytoplasm that plays a central role in immunity.

Lysosome (LI-so-som): A cellular organelle that contains digestive enzymes.

M

Macrophage (MAK-ro-faj): A large phagocytic cell that originated from a monocyte.

Macula (MAK-yoo-la): One of the sensory structures in the vestibule of the inner ear. It serves as a receptor for static equilibrium.

Macula lutea (MAK-yoo-la LOO-te-a): A yellow-colored depression in the retina of the eye.

Malleus (MAL-e-us): The lateral ear bone that contacts the tympanic membrane; the hammer.

Mammary (MAM-a-re) **gland**: A modified sweat gland in the breast that serves as the gland of milk secretion for nourishment of the young.

Matrix (MA-triks): The intercellular material in connective tissue.

Mastication (mas'-ti-KA-shun): A synonym for the muscular act of chewing.

Medial (ME-de-al): A directional term describing a part lying nearer to the vertical midline of the body relative to another part.

Mediastinum (me'-de-as-TI-num): A partition between the two peural cavities in the chest that consists of the heart, part of the esophagus, part of the trachea, and the major vessels of the heart.

Medulla (me-DUL-a): An inner, or deeper, part of an organ. For example, the medulla of the kidneys and the medulla of the adrenal gland.

Medulla oblongata (me-DUL-a ob'-long-GA-ta): The inferior part of the brain stem.

Medullary cavity (med-YOO-lar-e KAV-i-te): The potential space within the shaft of a long bone that contains yellow marrow.

Membrane (MEM-bran): A thin sheet of tissue that lines or covers body structures. It may contain a thin layer of epithelial tissue and connective tissue, or only connective tissue.

Membranous labyrinth (MEM-bra-nus LAB-i-rinth): The portion of the inner ear located inside the bony labyrinth that contains perilymph fluid. It consists of the membranous semicircular canals, the saccule and utricle, and the cochlear duct.

Meninges (me-NIN-jez): The three membranes covering the brain and spinal cord.

Mesentery (MES-en-ter'-e): A fold of the peritoneum that attaches the small intestine to the posterior abdominal wall.

Metabolism (me-TAB-o-lizm): The sum of all chemical reactions occurring in the body, including anabolic (synthetic) and catabolic (decomposition) reactions.

Metacarpus (met'-a-KAR-pus): A collective term for the five bones (each of which is called a metacarpal) of the palm of the hand.

Metatarsus (MET-a-tar-sus): A collective term for the five bones (each of which is called a metatarsal) of the foot.

Microvilli (mi'-kro-VIL-i): Microscopic extensions of the cell membrane filled with cytoplasm that serve to increase the absorptive surface area of the cell.

Micturition (mik'-too-RISH-un): The act of discharging urine from the urinary bladder to the exterior. Also called urination.

Midbrain (MID-bran): The superior part of the brain stem, located between the diencephalon and the pons. It serves as a relay center for impulses. Also called the mesencephalon.

Middle ear: The area of the ear between the tympanic membrane of the outer ear and the bony labyrinth of the inner ear. It is an epithelial-lined space that houses the three ear ossicles. Also called the tympanic cavity.

Midsagittal (MID-sag-i-tal): A plane that extends vertically through the body, dividing it into unequal right and left portions.

Mitochondrion (mit'-o'-KON-dre-on): A cellular organelle that consists of a double layer of plasma membrane where many of the catabolic activities of the cell take place.

Mitosis (mi-TO-sis): The division of a cell's nucleus into two daughter nuclei, each of which contain the same genetic composition as the original parent. When mitosis is followed by cytokinesis, equal division of the whole cell results.

Mitral valve (MI-tral valv): A synonym for the left atrioventricular valve. Also called the bicuspid valve.

Mons pubis (monz PYOO-bis): The elevated, hair-covered body surface area over the symphysis pubis in females.

Mucosa (myoo-KO-sa): An epithelial membrane that lines a body cavity or organ and contains cells that secrete mucus. Also called mucous membrane.

Mucus (MYOO-kus): A thick fluid secretion from mucous cells.

Muscle: An organ composed of skeletal muscle tissue and its associated connective tissue that functions mainly in the production of movement of the skeleton.

Muscle fiber: A synonym for muscle cell.

Muscle tissue: One of the four primary types of tissue in the body, characterized by its specialization to contract.

Muscularis (mus'-kyoo-LAR-is): A layer of smooth muscle tissue within the wall of an organ.

Myelin sheath (MI-e-lin sheth): A white, segmented insulative cover over the axons of many peripheral neurons that is produced by Schwann cells. A neuron axon that is covered by the myelin sheath is said to be myelinated.

Myocardium (mi'-o-KAR-de-um): The primary layer of the heart wall, which is composed of cardiac muscle tissue.

Myofibril (mi'-o-FI-bril): A rod-shaped component of a muscle fiber, which extends the length of the fiber and is composed of thin and thick filaments of protein.

Myometrium (mi'-o-ME-tre-um): The smooth muscle layer in the wall of the uterus.

N

Nail: A thin, hard plate of mostly keratin that is derived from the epidermis and develops atthe distal end of the fingers and toes.

Nasal cavity: The space within the nose that is lined with mucous membrane and divided by the nasal septum into right and left chambers.

Nasal septum: A vertical partition dividing the nasal cavity into right and left chambers that is composed of bone and cartilage covered with mucous membrane.

Nasopharynx (na'-so-FAR-inks): The superior portion of the pharynx, which transports air between the internal nares and the oropharynx.

Nephron (NE-fron): One of many microscopic, tubular structures within each kidney where the functions of filtration, reabsorption, and secretion occur.

Nerve: An organ of the nervous system composed of a bundle of neuron axons invested and surrounded by connective tissue and blood vessels, which functions in the conduction of an impulse from one area of the body to another.

Nerve impulse: A wave of negative charges (depolarization) that propagates along the outer surface of the plasma membrane of a conductive cell, such as a neuron. Also called an action potential.

Neurilemma (noo'-ri-LEM-a): The outer layer of a myelin sheath associated with a nerve fiber that contains the nucleus and much of the cytoplasm of a Schwann cell.

Neuroglia (noo'-ROG-le-a): Supportive cells of the nervous system that are most prevalent in the brain and spinal cord.

Neuromuscular junction (noo'-ro-MUS-kyoo-lar JUNK-shun): The area of contact between the terminal end of a motor neuron and the sarcolemma of a skeletal muscle fiber.

Neuron (NOO-ron): A cell of nerve tissue characterized by its specialization to conduct impulses (conductivity).

Neurotransmitter (noo'-ro-TRANS-mit-er): A molecule that transmits or inhibits the transmission of a nerve impulse from one neuron to another across a synapse.

Neutrophil (NOO-tro-fil): A type of granular, phagocytic white blood cell characterized by a cytoplasm that stains pink in a neutral stain.

Node of Ranvier (ran'-ve-A): A gap in the myelin sheath covering a nerve fiber, which accelerates the rate of impulse conduction.

Nucleolus (noo-KLE-o-lus): A spherical body within the nucleus of a cell that is not bound by a plasma membrane, which functions in the storage of ribosomal RNA.

Nucleus (NOO-kle-us): The largest structure in a cell, it contains the genetic material to determine protein structure and function, the DNA, and is enveloped by a double-layered plasma membrane.

O

Occipital (ok-SIP-i-tal): Pertaining to the lower back portion of the head.

Olfactory (ol-FAK-tor-e): Pertaining to the sense of smell.

Oocyte (O-o-sit): A gamete produced within an ovary. Also called ovum or egg.

Optic (OP-tik): Pertaining to the sense of vision or to the eye.

Optic chiasma (OP-tik ki-AZ-ma): The point at which the two optic nerves cross on the ventral aspect of the brain.

Optic disk: The area on the retina where the optic nerve exits the eye and contains no rod or cone cells. Also called the blind spot.

Orbit (OR-bit): One of two large depressions in the skull that is bordered by seven bones and houses the eyeball and associated structures. Also called the eye socket.

Organ (OR-gan): An organized combination of two or more different types of tissues that performs a general function.

Organ of Corti (KOR-ti): The structure within the inner ear that contains receptor cells sensitive to sound vibrations.

Organelle (or-gan-EL): A component of a cell that has a consistent, similar structure in other cells and performs a particular function.

Organic (or-GAN-ik): A chemical substance whose structure is based on a carbon skeleton.

Organism (OR-gan-izm): A complete living being; a whole individual.

Orifice (OR-i-fis): An opening into the body or into a structure.

Origin (OR-i-jin): The point of attachment of a muscle's tendon to a stationary bone.

Oropharynx (or'-o-FAR-inks): The middle portion of the pharynx, located between the nasopharynx and the laryngopharynx. The oral cavity opens into it (by way of the fauces).

Osseous (OS-e-us): Pertaining to bone.

Ossification (os'-i-fi-KA-shun): Bone formation. Also called osteogenesis.

Osteoblast (OS-te-o-blast'): A type of bone cell characterized by its mobility and by its ability to produce bone matrix.

Osteoclast (OS-te-o-klast'): A type of bone cell characterized by its ability to dissolve bone matrix.

Osteocyte (OS-te-o-sit'): A type of bone cell characterized by its immobile location within a lacunus and by a reduced ability to produce bone matrix.

Osteon (OS-te-on): An organized arrangement of bone tissue in adult compact bone such that the bone matrix concentrically surrounds a central canal containing a blood vessel. Also called a Haversian system.

Otic (O-tik): Pertaining to the ear.

Oval window: The membrane-covered opening between the stapes and the inner ear.

Ovary (O-var-e): The female gonad, or primary reproductive organ that produces gametes and female sex hormones.

Ovulation (ov-yoo-LA-shun): The release of a secondary oocyte from a Graafian follicle in an ovary.

P

Pacinian corpuscle (pa-SIN-e-an KOR-pus-el): A receptor located in the dermis that responds to touch (pressure).

Palate (PAL-at): The mucous membrane-lined structure forming the roof of the mouth. The anterior end is the hard palate, and the posterior end is the soft palate.

Pancreas (PAN-kre-as): A soft, oblong organ located posterior to the stomach in the abdominal cavity. The pancreas secretes digestive enzymes and hormones that regulate blood sugar.

Papilla (pa-PIL-a): A small finger-shaped projection.

Parasagittal (par'-a-SAJ-i-tal): A plane that extends vertically through the body dividing it into unequal right and left portions.

Parasympathetic division (par'-a-simp-a-THE-tik di-VI-zhun): The component of the autonomic nervous system that stimulates activities that conserve body energy.

Parathyroid (par'-a-THI-royd) **gland**: One of four or five pea-shaped glands embedded into the posterior side of the thyroid gland.

Parietal (pa-RI-e-tal): Pertaining to the outer wall of a cavity or organ.

Parietal cell: A cell in the stomach mucosa that secretes hydrochloric acid and intrinsic factor

Parietal pericardium (par'-i-KAR-de-um): The outer serous membrane covering the heart. Also called the pericardial sac.

Parietal peritoneum (par'-i-to-NE-um): The outer serous membrane covering attached to the walls of the abdominopelvic cavity.

Parietal pleura (PLOO-ra): The outer serous membrane associated with each lung. It is attached to the inner thoracic wall.

Parotid (pa-ROT-id) **glands**: A pair of salivary glands, each of which is located between the skin of the cheek and the masseter muscle on a side of the face.

Pectoral (PEK-tor-al): Pertaining to the ventral thorax, or chest.

Pelvic (PEL-vik): Pertaining to the base of the trunk region, or pelvis.

Pelvic cavity: The inferior portion of the abdominopelvic cavity bordered by the pelvis.

Pelvis: The bowl-like base axial skeleton formed by the two pelvic (innominate) bones and the sacrum.

Penis (PE-nis): The external reproductive organ of the male through which most of the urethra extends.

Pepsin (PEP-sin): An enzyme initially secreted by zymogenic (chief) cells in the stomach mucosa in the inactive form of pepsinogen that, when activated by the presence of hydrochloric acid into pepsin, can digest protein.

Pericardial (par'-i-KAR-de-al) **cavity**: A narrow space between the outer wall of the heart (the visceral pericardium) and the parietal pericardium that contains pericardial fluid.

Pericardium (par'-i-KAR-de-um): The serous membrane associated with the heart that is composed of two layers, an inner visceral pericardium and an outer parietal pericardium.

Perichondrium (par'-i-KON-dre-um): A layer of dense connective tissue that envelopes cartilage.

Perilymph (PAR-i-limf): The fluid within the membranous labyrinth of the inner ear.

Perimysium (par'-i-MI-se-um): An extension of the epimysium of muscle that invaginates inward to divide a muscle into bundles.

Perineum (par'-i-NE-um): The area between the anus and the posterior border of the external genitalia.

Perineurium (par'-i-NYOO-re-um): An extension of the epineurium of a nerve that invaginates inward to wrap around bundles of nerve fibers.

Periosteum (par'-e-OS-te-um): The connective tissue covering around a bone that is important in bone growth, nutrition, and repair.

Peripheral (per-I-fer-al) **nervous system (PNS):** The division of the nervous system consisting of nerves and ganglia located between the central nervous system and the body surfaces.

Peritoneum (par'-i-to-NE-um): The extensive serous membrane associated with the abdominopelvic cavity.

Peritoneal (par'-i-to-NE-al) **cavity:** The space between the parietal peritoneum and the visceral peritoneum that contains a small amount of fluid.

Peyer's patches: Clusters of lymphatic tissue containing numerous white blood cells that are located in the wall of the small intestine.

Phalanx (FA-lanks): A bone of a digit (finger or toe). Plural form is phalanges.

Pharynx (FAR-inks): A tube that extends from the level of the internal nares to its union with the larynx, which transports air, food, and liquid.

Pia mater (PE-a MA-ter): The innermost of the three meninges surrounding the brain and spinal cord.

Pineal (pi-NE-al) **gland:** A small endocrine gland located at the posterior end of the diencephalon, forming a part of the roof of the third ventricle.

Pituitary (pi-TOO-i-tar-e) **gland:** A small, functionally important endocrine gland located inferior to the hypothalamus and attached to it by way of a short stalk. Also called the hypophysis.

Placenta (pla-SEN-ta): A structure whose origin is shared by embryonic cells and the uterine lining that provides a means of material transport between the mother and developing unborn child.

Plasma (PLAZ-ma): The extracellular fluid that forms a portion of blood.

Plasma cell: A differentiated white blood cell that secretes antibodies.

Plasma membrane: A microscopic barrier associated with cells composed mainly of a phospholipid bilayer and protein. The outer plasma membrane of a cell is also called the cell membrane.

Platelet (PLA-te-let): A formed element of blood that is active in blood clot formation.

Pleura (PLOOR-a): The serous membrane associated with the lungs. It consists of an inner visceral pleural and an outer parietal pleura. Plural form is pleurae.

Pleural cavity: A narrow space between the visceral and parietal pleurae that contains pleural fluid.

Plexus (PLEKS-us): A network of interconnecting nerves, veins, or lymphatic vessels.

Pons (ponz): A part of the brain located between the midbrain and the medulla oblongata.

Popliteal (pop'-li-TE-al): Pertaining to the area posterior to the knee joint.

Posterior (po-STER-e-or): A directional term describing the location of a part being toward the back or rear side relative to another part. In humans it is also known as dorsal.

Posterior horn: A region of the spinal cord gray matter containing sensory neuron cell bodies. Also called the ventral horn.

Posterior root: The structure merging with the spinal cord on its posterior aspect that contains sensory nerves. Also called the dorsal root.

Prepuce (PRE-poos): The skin that partially covers the glans of the penis (in the male) or clitoris (in the female).

Process (PRO-ses): A prominent projection on a bone.

Pronation (pro-NA-shun): Movement of the hand such that the palm is turned downward (inferiorly) or backward (posteriorly).

Prostate (PRO-stat) **gland:** A walnut-shaped gland surrounding the urethra as it emerges from the urinary bladder in males. Its secretions contribute to semen.

Protein (PRO-ten): An organic compound composed of amino acid subunits.

Proximal (PROKS-i-mal): A directional term indicating a body part that is located nearer to the origin or point of attachment to the trunk than another; opposite of distal.

Pulmonary circulation: The circuit of blood flow to the lungs, through lung capillaries, and back to the left atrium of the heart.

Pupil (PYOO-pil): The small hole through the center of the iris in the eye through which light passes.

Pyloric sphincter (pi-LOR-ik SFINC-ter): A circular band of smooth muscle at the union of the stomach and small intestine that controls the movement of material between them. Also called the pyloric valve.

R

Receptor (re-SEP-tor): A structure that is capable of responding to a stimulus by initiating a nerve impulse.

Rectum (REK-tum): The distal portion of the large intestine.

Renal (RE-nal): Pertaining to the kidneys.

Renal corpuscle (KOR-pus-el): The portion of a kidney nephron consisting of the Bowman's capsule and glomerulus.

Renal pelvis (PEL-vis): A membrane-lined basin within the renal sinus of each kidney.

Renal pyramid (PIR-a-mid): One of about eight to ten cone-shaped structures in each kidney extending from the medulla to the cortex, which contain the renal tubules.

Renal sinus (SI-nus): A potential space within each kidney extending from the hilum to the medulla, which contains the renal pelvis.

Renal tubule (TOO-byool): A part of a nephron of the kidney consisting of a microscopic tube extending from Bowman's capsule to a collecting duct. The functions of reabsorption and secretion occur across its walls.

Respiratory membrane: The barrier in the lungs that must be crossed by gas molecules during gas exchange. It consists of the alveolar epithelium, a basement membrane, and the endothelium of a capillary.

Retina (RET-i-na): The light-sensitive inner layer of the eye that contains rod and cone cells.

Retroperitoneal (re'-tro-par'-i-to-NE-al): Pertaining to a structure lying external to the parietal peritoneum.

Ribosome (RI-bo-som): A microscopic, spherical structure within the cytoplasm of a cell composed of RNA and protein that serves as an attachment site for messenger RNA during protein synthesis.

Rod cell: A photoreceptor cell in the retina of the eye that detects very low levels of light.

Rotator cuff: A group of four muscles that attach the humerus to the scapula.

Rotation (ro-TA-shun): The movement of a bone around its own (longitudinal) axis.

Round window: The membrane-covered opening between the middle ear and the inner ear that is not in contact with the auditory ossicles.

Rugae (ROO-je): Folds or ridges in the mucosa of an organ with a large lumen, such as the stomach or vagina.

S

Saccule (SAK-yool): One of two sacs within the vestibule of the inner ear that houses the receptors of static equilibrium.

Sagittal (SAJ-i-tal): A vertical plane that divides the body into right and left portions, and includes the midsagittal plane (dividing into equal halves) and the parasagittal plane (dividing into unequal portions).

Saliva (sa-LI-va): A fluid secretion by the salivary glands deposited into the mouth to lubricate and begin digestion of food before swallowing.

Salivary (SAL-i-var-e) **gland:** One of several exocrine glands in the facial region that secrete saliva into the mouth to initiate the digestive process.

Sarcolemma (sar'-ko-LEM-a): The plasma membrane covering the outer surface of a muscle fiber.

Sarcomere (SAR-ko-mer): A contractile microscopic subunit of striated muscle (skeletal and cardiac muscle tissue).

Sarcoplasm (SAR-ko-plazm): The cytoplasm of a muscle fiber.

Schwann cell: A type of neuroglial cell that forms myelin sheaths around axons of peripheral nerves.

Sclera (SKLE-ra): The posterior part of the outer, fibrous tunic covering the eyeball; the white of the eye.

Scrotum (SKRO-tum): An external genital organ of the male consisting of a skin-covered sack that contains the testes.

Sebaceous (se-BA-shus) **gland**: An exocrine gland located in the dermis that secretes an oily substance called sebum. It is usually associated with a hair follicle.

Sebum (SE-bum): An oily secretion of a sebaceous gland.

Secretion (se-KRE-shun): A substance produced and released by a cell that serves a useful benefit.

Semen (SE-men): A reproductive fluid discharged by a male during ejaculation that contains sperm cells and secretions from the seminal vesicles, prostate gland, and bulbourethral glands.

Semicircular canal (se'-mi-SER-kyoo-lar ca-NAL): One of three looping canals in each temporal bone that form a part of the inner ear. It contains perilymph fluid and the receptors for equilibrium.

Semilunar (SL) valve (sem-i-LOO-nar valv): One of two heart valves located between a ventricle and a major artery. The aortic valve is located between the left ventricle and aorta, and the pulmonary valve is located between the right ventricle and pulmonary trunk.

Seminal vesicle (SEM-i-nal VES-i-kel): One of a pair of convoluted glands of the male reproductive system located posterior to the urinary bladder that secretes part of the semen.

Seminiferous tubule (sem'-i-NIF-er-us TOO-byool): A microscopic, tightly packed tube within each testis where sperm cells develop.

Septum (SEP-tum): A barrier between two spaces, such as the interventricular septum of the heart and the nasal septum.

Serosa (ser-O-sa): Any serous membrane. Also, the outer serous membrane layer of a visceral organ.

Serous membrane (SER-us MEM-bran): An epithelial membrane that lines a body cavity or covers an organ, and secretes small amounts of fluid.

Sesamoid (SES-a-moyd) **bones**: Small bones formed and located within major tendons or ligaments. For example, the patella (kneecap) is a sesamoid bone.

Sigmoid colon (SIG-moyd KO-lon): The distal segment of the colon located between the descending colon and the rectum.

Sinoatrial node (sin'-o-A-tre-al nod) (SA node): A cluster of specialized cardiac muscle cells in the wall of the right atrium that initiate each cardiac cycle.

Sinus (SI-nus): A space within a bone lined with mucous membrane, such as the frontal and maxillary sinuses in the head. Also, a modified vein with an enlarged lumen for blood storage.

Skeletal muscle tissue: One of three types of muscle tissue in the body characterized by the presence of visible striations and conscious control over its contraction. It attaches to bones to form the muscles of the body.

Skull: The group of bones that make up the supporting framework and body of the head.

Small intestine: The organ of the alimentary canal located between the stomach and the large intestine that functions in the final digestion and absorption of nutrients.

Smooth muscle: One of three types of muscle tissue in the body characterized by the lack of visible striations and unconscious control over its contraction. It forms part of the walls of hollow organs and blood vessels.

Soft palate: The posterior portion of the bridge forming the roof of the mouth, consisting of skeletal muscle covered with mucous membrane.

Somatic (so-MA-tik): Pertaining to the body. For example, a somatic cell is any body cell other than a sex cell.

Somatic nervous system: The component of the peripheral nervous system that conveys impulses associated with conscious sensory and motor activities.

Spermatic cord (sper-MA-tik kord): A narrow bundle of tissue in the male reproductive system extending from the epididymis to the inguinal canal, consisting of the ductus deferens, cremaster muscle, blood vessels, lymphatics, nerves, and connective tissue.

Spermatozoa (sper-ma'-to-ZO-a): The male gametes, or reproductive cells. Also called sperm cells. Singular form is spermatozoon.

Sphincter (SFENK-ter): A circular band of smooth muscle surrounding an opening, which serves to control the movement of materials through.

Spinal cord: A long, narrow organ of the central nervous system that extends through the vertebral canal and connects the peripheral nervous system with the brain.

Spinal nerve: One of 31 pairs of nerves that extend between the spinal cord and another part of the body.

Spleen: An soft, glandular organ that is part of the lymphatic system and is located in the upper left region of the abdomen behind the stomach.

Spongy bone: One of two types of bone tissue, characterized by the presence of spaces filled with red marrow between thin bone spicules called trabeculae.

Stomach (STO-muk): A large, hollow organ in the alimentary canal located between the esophagus and small intestine that plays a prominent role in digestion.

Subarachnoid space (sub-a-RAK-noyd spas): The narrow space between the arachnoid and pia mater surrounding the brain and spinal cord, which contains circulating cerebrospinal fluid.

Subcutaneous layer (sub'-kyoo-TA-ne-us LAyer): The layer of loose connective tissue and adipose tissue deep to the dermis of the skin. Also called hypodermis, and superficial fascia.

Sublingual (sub-LING-wal) glands: A pair of salivary glands located in the floor of the mouth deep to the mucous membrane.

Submandibular (sub'-man-DIB-yoo-lar) **glands:** A pair of salivary glands located along the inner surface of the jaw in the floor of the mouth. Also called submaxillary glands.

Submucosa (sub'-myoo-KO-sa): A layer of connective tissue located external to a mucous membrane.

Sudoriferous (soo'-dor-I-fer-us) **gland:** An exocrine gland located in the skin that secretes sweat. Also called sweat gland.

Sulcus (SUL-kus): A shallow groove or depression.

Superficial (soo'-per-FISH-al): A directional term indicating the location of a part that is toward or nearer to the body surface relative to another.

Superior (soo-PER-e-or): A directional term indicating the location of a part that is nearer to the head region than another. Also called craniad or cephalad.

Supination (soo'-pi-NA-shun): The rotation of the forearm such that the palm of the hand is turned anteriorly or superiorly.

Suture (SOO-cher): A type of tight-fitting fibrous joint that permits little or no movement between opposing bones.

Sweat gland: An exocrine gland located in the skin that secretes sweat. Also called sudoriferous gland.

Sympathetic division (simp'-a-THE-tik di-VI-zhun): A division of the autonomic nervous system that functions mainly in stimulating emergency responses (fight or flight).

Synapse (sin-APS): The junction between the axon of one neuron and the dendrite or cell body of another neuron.

Synergist (SIN-er-jist): A muscle in a group action that assists the prime mover by keeping other structures stable.

Synovial joint (sin-O-ve-al joynt): A type of joint characterized by the presence of a membrane-lined cavity, called the synovial cavity, between opposing bones.

Synovial fluid: The liquid secretion of epithelial cells in the synovial membrane lining a synovial joint, which serves as a lubricant and shock absorber.

System (SIS-tem): An organized combination of organs and associated structures that share a common function.

Systemic circulation: The major circulatory network of the body that carries oxygenated blood from the left ventricle throughout the body (except the lungs), and returns deoxygenated blood to the right atrium.

T

Tarsus (TAR-sus): The seven bones of the ankle as a collective unit.

Tectorial membrane (tek-TOR-e-al MEM-bran): A thin membrane in the inner ear that projects over the receptor hair cells of the organ of Corti.

Tendon (TEN-don): A band of dense connective tissue that extends from the muscle to attach to a bone.

Testis (TES-tis): One of a pair of male gonads (sex glands) located within the scrotum that produces sperm cells and testosterone. Plural form is testes.

Thalamus (THAL-a-mus): A bilobed endocrine gland located in the anterior neck region that produces hormones influencing growth and metabolism, and maintains calcium levels in the blood.

Thoracic cavity (tho-RAS-ik CAV-i-te): The part of the anterior (ventral) body cavity located superior to the diaphragm.

Thoracic duct: The main collecting trunk of the lymphatic circulation, which extends along the back of the chest to the right subclavian vein. It drains lymph from all areas of the body but the right side of the head, neck, chest, and right arm.

Thorax (THOR-aks): The region of the trunk located superior to the diaphragm. Also called the chest.

Thrombocyte (THROM-bo-sit): The formed elements in blood that play a prominent role in blood clotting. Also called platelets.

Thymus (THI-mus) **gland:** A glandular lymphatic organ located superior to the heart that produces T lymphocytes during early childhood, and degenerates by adulthood.

Thyroid cartilage (THI-royd CAR-ti-lij): The largest piece of hyaline cartilage of the larynx. Also called Adam's apple.

Thyroid gland: An endocrine gland located on the anterior side of the neck that secretes hormones involved in growth and metabolism, and maintains calcium levels in the blood.

Tissue (TI-shoo): A group of similar cells that combine to form a common function.

Tongue (tung): The muscular organ of the digestive system that is anchored to the floor of the mouth and wall of the pharynx, and which plays a role in swallowing and speech formation.

Tonsil (TON-sil): A small organ of the lymphatic system that consists of an aggregation of fixed lymphocytes and connective tissue embedded in a mucous membrane. There are three pairs (pharyngeal, palatine, and lingual), all of which play a role in the immune response.

Trabecula (tra-BEK-yoo-la): A thin plate of bone within spongy bone tissue. Also, a band of supportive connective tissue extending to the interior of an organ from its outer wall.

Trachea (TRA-ke-a): An organ of the respiratory system that consists of a long tube supported by rings of cartilage extending from the pharynx to the bronchi.

Transverse colon (TRANS-vers KO-lon): The segment of the colon that extends from its union with the ascending colon to its union with the descending colon.

Tricuspid valve (tri-KUS-pid valv): The heart valve located between the right atrium and right ventricle. Also called the right atrioventricular (AV) valve.

Trunk: The region of the body to which the appendages are attached, and includes the chest, abdomen, and back.

Tubercle (TOO-ber-kul): A small, rounded process on the surface of a bone.

Tympanic membrane (tim-PAN-ik MEM-bran): A thin membrane between the external auditory canal and the tympanic cavity, separating the external ear from the middle ear. Also called the eardrum.

U

Umbilical cord (um-BIL-i-kal kord): The rope-like structure containing the umbilical arteries and umbilical vein that connects a fetus with the placenta.

Ureter (YOO-re-ter): A long, narrow tube that extends from a kidney to the urinary bladder and transports urine.

Urethra (yoo-RE-thra): A tube extending from the urinary bladder to the exterior that carries urine in females and urine and semen in males.

Urinary bladder (yoo'-ri-NAR-e BLAD-der): A hollow muscular organ located at the floor of the pelvic cavity that temporarily stores urine.

Urine (YOO-rin): The fluid produced by the kidneys that is expelled out the urethra and contains water, metabolic waste materials, and excess salts.

Uterine tube (YOO-ter-in toob): One of two tubes that transport ova from the ovaries to the uterus in the female reproductive system. Also called fallopian tubes or oviducts.

Uterus (YOO-ter-us): A hollow muscular organ in the female reproductive system that serves as a site of embryo implantation and development, and menstruation.

Uvula (YOO-vyoo-la): A fingerlike projection of skeletal muscle covered with mucous membrane at the posterior end of the soft palate.

V

Vagina (va-JI-na): A tubular, muscular organ of the female reproductive system extending between the vulva and the uterus.

Vascular (VAS-kyoo-lar): Pertaining to or containing blood vessels.

Vein (van): A blood vessel that transports blood from body tissues to the heart.

Ventral (VEN-tral): A directional term describing the location of a part nearer to the anterior, or front side, of the body relative to another. Also called anterior.

Ventral cavity: The body cavity located on the anterior side of the trunk containing the thoracic and abdominopelvic cavities.

Ventral root: The motor branch of a spinal nerve that connects with the spinal cord.

Ventricle (VEN-tri-kul): One of the two inferior, highly muscular chambers of the heart that push blood into major arteries during their contraction.

Venule (VEN-yool): A small vein that collects deoxygenated blood from a capillary network and conveys it to a larger vein.

Vermiform appendix (VER-mi-form a-PEN-diks): A small, closed-end tube extending from the cecum of the large intestine.

Vermis (VER-mis): The central constricted part of the cerebellum that separates the two cerebellar hemispheres.

Vertebral canal (VER-te-bral ka-NAL): A cavity extending through the vertebral column that is formed by the vertebral foramina of each vertebra, through which extends the spinal cord.

Vertebral column: The skeleton of the back that is composed of 26 vertebrae and associated tissues. Also called the backbone, spine, or spinal column.

Vesicle (VES-i-kul): A small sac containing a fluid. In the cell, it is a membranous sac within the cytoplasm that contains cellular products or waste materials.

Vestibule (VES-ti-byool): A small space that opens into a larger cavity or canal. A vestibule is found in the inner ear, mouth, nose, and vagina.

Villus (VIL-lus): A small, fingerlike projection of the small intestinal wall that contains connective tissue, blood vessels, and a lymphatic vessel, and which functions in the absorption of nutrients. Plural form is villi.

Visceral (VIS-er-al): Pertaining to the internal components (mainly the organs) of a body cavity; pertaining to the outer surface of an internal organ.

Visceral peritoneum (par'-i-to-NE-um): A serous membrane that covers the surfaces of abdominal organs.

Visceral pleura (PLOO-ra): A serous membrane that covers the outer surface of each lung.

Vitreous humor (VI-tre-us HYOO-mer): A mass of gelatinous material located within the eyeball in the posterior cavity located between the lens and the retina. Also called vitreous body.

Vocal cords (VO-kal kordz): Folds of mucous membrane within the larynx that produce sound when they vibrate.

Vulva (VUL-va): The external genitalia of the female reproductive system. Also called pudendum.

W

White matter: A type of nerve tissue composed mainly of the myelinated axons of neurons.

Y

Yellow marrow: A collection of fat storage (adipose) and other tissues found within the medullary cavities of bones.

Z

Zygote (ZI-got): The single, fertilized cell resulting from the union of an oocyte with a sperm cell.

Zymogenic (zi'-mo-GEN-ik) **cell**: A cell within a gastric gland of the stomach mucosa that secretes a precursor protein, pepsinogen.